Children and Technology

Children and Technology

Katrina Blythe
with Richard Bennett and Andrew Hamill

Nash Pollock Publishing

© 1996 Katrina Blythe, Richard Bennett, Andrew Hamill

First published in 1996 by
Nash Pollock Publishing
32 Warwick Street
Oxford OX4 1SX

9 8 7 6 5 4 3 2 1

Orders to:
9 Carlton Close
Grove
Wantage
Oxfordshire OX12 0PU

The authors' moral rights are asserted.

A catalogue record of this book is available from the British Library.

ISBN 1 898255 10 5

Typeset in 10.5/13 pt New Century Schoolbook, by Can Do Design, Buckingham.

Printed in Great Britain by Redwood Books, Trowbridge

Contents

Acknowledgements

This book has been written by tutors in the Department of Technology at Chester College. The department specialises in the training of intending primary school teachers, all of whom now have to study Technology as part of their degree programme. The book captures the enthusiasm and originality which children, students and teachers generate when engaged in technological activity. It reflects the philosophy and work of all those in the department and, in addition to the three principal authors, three other tutors, Carole Naylor, Tony Pickford and Malcolm Glover have contributed to the book.

Katrina Blythe
Head of Technology

The authors would like to thank the teachers and children from the following schools for their assistance in the production of this book:
Blacon Hall Junior School, Chester
Boughton Heath Primary School, Chester
Cherry Grove Primary School, Chester
Daresbury County Primary School, Cheshire
Dee Point Primary School, Chester
Great Bollington CE Primary School, Cheshire
Harthill County Primary School, Cheshire
Highfield Junior School, Chester
Manley County Primary School, Cheshire
Moore County Primary School, Cheshire
Oldfield County Primary School, Cheshire
St Werburg County Primary School, Cheshire
Tarporley County Primary School, Cheshire
Waverton County Primary School, Cheshire
Woodfield Junior School, Chester

We should also like to thank our students and Anna Markus and Neenah Watson, professional puppeteers.

Primary Matters: Editors' Preface

It is hard to find an acknowledgement of how recent are primary schools whose curriculum and management reflect the particular emotional, social, intellectual and physical needs of young children, nor of how far they have developed in a very brief time span. Indeed, there are teachers in today's primary schools who remember that in 1949, five years after the famous Butler Education Act, 36% of children of secondary age were still attending schools which also housed children under 11. Those same teachers have seen the development of primary schools through the Plowden era in the 1960s, the building of open-plan schools which aroused such intense international interest in the 1960s and 70s, and in the 1980s and the 1988 Education Reform Act.

This Act made far-reaching changes. The introduction of a national curriculum was a radical development and brought in its wake consequences unforseen by its designers. Teachers were quick to discover that the syllabi which had been constructed in such detail were impossible to build into an effective curriculum; tests for 7 and 11 year olds which had been devised to give the curriculum credibility became a focus for parental and professional discontent. Persistent re-writes led finally to a 'reform' of the new curriculum by the Dearing Committee in the early 1990s. This was an attempt to make manageable what was unmanageable, hastily introduced and overburdened with bureaucracy.

These recent changes and upheavals must be set against the slow emergence of a realisation that the needs and aspirations of young people are not necessarily the same at 7 as they are at 13, and that the way in which knowledge is acquired and becomes useful must relate to particular phases in personal development and rhythms of growth.

In the years following the first world war, successive Government committees examined the educational needs of adolescents, of boys and girls in the middle years of childhood (7-11) and of children of infant and nursery age. These committees reported between 1926 and 1933 and their recommendations, though implemented in a piecemeal fashion, did lead to a considerable restructuring of schooling in England and Wales. The most profound effect of these changes was the acknowledgement that the primary years were a coherent and essential stage in the education process, and a stage which had distinctive needs and requirements. Before this children had been educated in all-age schools. Unless a child was fortunate to be selected at the age of 11 (usually as a successful outcome of academic competition), the school s/he joined at 5 years of age would be the school s/he left at 13. 90% of the school population attended such schools and it became increasingly obvious that they were failing to meet the different needs of the 5 year old, the child in middle years, and of the 13 year old school leaver. In the late `1930s primary schools began to develop, with secondary (elementary) schools providing for those children who failed the selective examination. The distinctive categories of secondary education were enshrined in the 1944 Education Act which established a comprehensive tri-partite system of secondary education, but even five years later this was still not fully realised.

It took, therefore, some twenty years from the mid-1930s until the 1950s and 60s for primary schools to become generally established and, with the population explosion of the 50s and 60s, primary school practice underwent many developments as the early years of schooling came to be regarded as an essential phase in the educational process. Experiments were undertaken in teaching and learning methodology, in the curriculum, in the organisation of classes (remember vertical or family grouping?), and, as already mentioned, in the architectural style of new schools. The curriculum became richer and more challenging to young children. Enthusiastic support for these changes was found in the report published by the Plowden Committee in 1967.

In contrast to this period, more recently primary education has been subject to critical appraisal and retrenchment. Academics (like Peters and Dearden), and politicians (like Boyson and Cox), as well as inspectors from local education authorities and Her Majesty's Inspectorate, and more recently the Office for Standards in Education (OFSTED) have focused attention upon the issues and assumptions underlying the work offered by teachers to young children. Are there things which *all* children should learn during their primary years? What constitutes essential knowledge for the primary-age child? What should be the balance between the teaching of facts, the development of skills, the understanding of the concepts which underlie knowledge, and the processes through which this knowledge is acquired and developed? How effective are different classroom approaches in developing thinking skills, social awareness and responsibility? How can the primary curriculum best address the fundamental technological changes brought about by the microchip? In what ways are social issues such as racism, sexism or disadvantage best addressed? How should the particular insights and experiences of the disabled child be incorporated? How can institutional barriers to the involvement of all interested parties, especially parents, in the education of each child be dismantled? How should religious education be handled within a society which is more and more secular but also no longer made up of only one major faith group?

Questions such as these are not asked in a vacuum. They reflect the anxieties (real and imagined) of parents, academics, politicians, employers, and, most of all, of the teachers themselves. That such questions are now being asked is, in part, a recognition of how far primary schools have come over the fifty or so years since they were first conceived. In a climate of concern and criticism, it is also easy to forget that British developments in primary education have been the focus of attention, respect and emulation in many other countries. Indeed, many have argued that it was a freedom from bureaucracy which gave English primary schools their unique character and made possible the kinds of thoughtful experiment which attracted an international reputation. At the same time, others have suggested that piecemeal development has led to idiosyncrasy. Hence the current demand for every school to follow a programme reflecting clearly defined national criteria. However, the need for the individual teacher to make choices, ask questions, and influence every child's development continues to be respected and, however centralised the curriculum may become, however much the school programme is evaluated, however regularly children are tested against performance norms, the thoughtful teacher will continue to ask questions about *what* John or Akbar, Mary or Mai-Lin will learn, how they will learn it, what particular needs they have and how their individual interests, attitudes and aptitudes can be accommodated into and contribute to the daily work of the classroom.

As we have already noted the national curriculum has undergone considerable changes since its implementation. Nevertheless it remains a reference point around which head teachers and subject co-ordinators construct the school experience offered to their pupils, a situation which is unlikely to change whatever party is in government. But the teacher is not powerless. The curriculum of a school has rightly been defied as 'everything that happens in a school day but leaves undefined the meanings which are constructed and attributed by the pupils'. Such definitions tend to embrace the content (the 'what'), the approaches to unspoken attitudes (the 'how'), and the learning strongly influenced by beliefs which underpin the relationship between school, home and community (the 'why'). The content (what should schools teach?) is the least difficult of these diverse elements to measure, although we have already noted the difficulties encountered by the national curriculum exercise. But what young people will learn by engaging with the content is not only problematic but a source of persistent questioning by effective teachers. The titles in this series acknowledge the centrality of subjects in any national curriculum but at the same time seek to show the many ways in which a prescribed curriculum can be vivified and enriched.

All the books in this series address aspects of the kinds of questions which teachers are asking as part of their concern to establish effective strategies for learning. Part of that concern focuses upon the links between the excitement of learning evidenced by young children, and the need to evaluate and maintain coherence in their experiences. Effective learning is the product of engagement as each member of the group struggles to make the learning process his or her own. At the same time, personal learning can still be limited unless it is placed in a broader context so that, for example, subject strands unite into a comprehensible and rational whole. Each author in this series seeks to indicate cross-curricular links, even though the titles indicate particular subject specialisms as starting points, so that the approach unifies rather than divides the child's experience of the curriculum.

As editors of this series, we wish to offer practising primary teachers a range of titles which recognises the complexity of the primary teacher's role. Each book gives shape and purpose to a specific curriculum area, dealing with issues which are particular to that specialism, presenting ideas for interesting and innovative practice in that area but, at the same time, emphasising the unity of the primary experience. Thus, each title is set against a broad canvas, that of the primary school as a living and vibrant place in which young children grow and learn.

Leone Burton

Henry Pluckrose

Introduction

Synthesising what is meant by technology is not easy. Different groups of people have different perceptions and a proliferation of definitions abound. There is greater consensus when it comes to design, most people viewing it as a creative process and many also as a special case of problem solving. The following definitions reflect our understanding of technology and design and are those on which this book is structured.

Technology is the application of scientific and related knowledge to a problem. The solution may lead to the creation of a new product or an improved procedure for making a product.

Design is the creative process through which that solution is achieved. It involves the application of technological and aesthetic principles to meet an identified need in an efficient, elegant way, compatible with its environment.

Design and Technology has much to bring to primary classrooms. Not only is there a strong case for Design and Technology as a body of learning with its own unique place in the curriculum, but there is a special case for Design and Technology in the primary curriculum based on strong beliefs about the way that children think and learn. It can be used to foster *learning by doing,* for it is by trying to shape and control our environment we learn more about what is possible, and what we can expect from materials, concepts and ourselves.

In this book we aim to address the issues which any school has to consider when drawing up a policy document for Design and Technology.

First, it is important to identify the knowledge, skills and understanding in Design and Technology which children need to develop an overall appreciation and competency.

Skills are required in:
~ designing
~ making

and *knowledge and understanding* of the following are needed;

~ properties of a range of materials and components and appropriate joining techniques

~ structures

~ energy sources

~ mechanisms

~ control systems.

But the development of such skills, knowledge and understanding is only part of the story. It needs to be put in the context of technology in everyday life, and as teachers we also need to develop children's understanding of wider issues such as:

~ the fact that technology arises out of people's response to meet identified needs, and that both the needs and the ways of satisfying them vary over time and across cultures

~ the overall impact of technology on people's lives and the environment

~ the constantly evolving nature of technology, and how adapting existing solutions from previous experiences to new situations is an integral feature of technologica progress.

Technologists are primarily problem solvers. To help foster a technological approach to working, it follows therefore that children should be given opportunities to identify their needs, develop ideas as to how these needs could be met, and make products to meet them. Because technology relies on the appliance of scientific skills and knowledge, children also need to be given activities which will develop their fundamental scientific and technological understanding. At all stages it is important to encourage children to consider the wider issues around technology. Without this kind of holistic approach, design and make activities end up by being divorced from true technological intent.

The book is structured into four parts. The first two chapters look at facets of technology and technologists at work in the world outside the classroom. They are designed to give a purpose to technological activity, and to paint the backcloth against which children's skills, knowledge and understanding can be developed. They are intended to provide the teacher with background information and raise issues which could be discussed with children.

Chapter 3 considers children of different ages at work as technologists. Building on the scientific and technical knowledge with which they are familiar, they bring different solutions to design and make products in response to identified needs.

Chapters 4–9 look systematically at the contents of primary design and technology by examining work which children aged 5 to 11 have undertaken in the various strands of skills, knowledge and understanding.

Finally chapters 10 and 11 consider curriculum planning and the way children's design and technology can be managed in the classroom and throughout the school.

1 Technology and society

Introduction

Pick up any book about technology and you will be likely to read a different account of what constitutes technology. One of the problems of introducing Technology to the curriculum of primary schools has been the uncertainty as to its definition. At one extreme technology conjures up images of complex electronic gadgetry, while at the other it is seen to encompass all human practical activity – from boiling water to landing a space craft on the moon. Mrs Beeton, the famous Victorian cook, has often been misquoted as saying – "In order to cook jugged hare ... first catch your hare." Similarly, it could be argued that, in order to teach something successfully, we must first know and understand what we are going to teach.

In the introduction, we presented the definition of technology on which this book is based, namely;

Technology is the application of scientific and related knowledge to a problem. The solution may lead to the creation of a new product or an improved procedure for making a product.

Take the problem of urban transport. In London, if one wants to reach a location, particularly when unfamiliar with the local geography, one is likely to hail a black taxi cab. In the main, these are diesel-driven vehicles purpose-built to a design which has developed over the years. Passengers, driver and luggage are catered for in separate compartments. The vehicle has a very tight turning circle, enabling it to turn round in a city street. A diesel engine is used as it is considered to be better able to cope with the patterns of driving associated with long hours of city driving. Also, in Britain, diesel fuel is readily available and relatively cheap.

In Georgian times, the same problem was solved by, among other things, a sedan chair. The passenger was protected from the elements in an enclosed compartment, and the driving power (two men) was readily and cheaply available.

In many Asian cities today, the problem of urban transport has been solved by the tricycle rickshaw. Cycles, being the most efficient form of transport in terms of energy consumption, provide an economical solution to the transportation problem where financial resources are limited and labour is in plentiful supply.

As can be seen from the above examples, the technology which is employed in solving a given problem has to take account of many factors, including the human resources available in the form of skills, knowledge and understanding, the physical resources such as materials and energy sources, financial costs, and what is considered to be culturally and aesthetically acceptable.

The same is, of course, no less true in the classroom. While a class of seven year olds may solve the problem of making vehicles by constructing push-along models by modifying and combining reclaimed or junk materials, a class of ten year olds may have sufficient skills, knowledge and understanding to make electrically powered vehicles from wood and plastic. In this way, children are acting 'as technologists' in the classroom culture. But this school activity needs to be set in the wider context of technology in society, to help foster in children that sense of excitement, curiosity and responsibility which technology brings to our lives.

The first two chapters of this book aim to put a few broad brush-strokes on this wider canvas and raise issues to stimulate technological debate in the classroom. For the purposes of clarity, the following convention will be used throughout this book: Technology (with a capital T) will refer to the school subject, whereas technology (with a lower case t) will represent the general term.

Factors affecting the choice of technological solutions to a problem

When comparing technological solutions from different cultures or periods in history, the factors affecting decisions tend to be readily apparent. But what of the reasons for different technological solutions when situations are similar? Take, for example, electricity generation in Britain and Denmark. The population's heating and energy requirements (per person) are similar in both countries, and yet the technological solutions chosen to generate electricity are markedly different. In Britain, 24% of the country's electricity is generated by nuclear power, whereas in Denmark the figure is 0%. In Britain, roughly 2% of electricity is generated from renewable sources, whereas Denmark produces 5% of its electricity from renewable sources and aims to increase this to around 10% by the turn of the century. Clearly, there are more criteria involved in making decisions than purely technical ones. In the case of the supply of electricity, political, environmental, ethical and social pressures influence technological choices. Denmark has made a political decision not to opt for nuclear power and, following the 1973 world oil crisis, has made a decision to reduce its reliance on imported energy sources. Having few non-renewable fuel resources to draw upon, the Danish government has made the decision to cut down energy usage throughout the country by passing legislation to encourage energy conservation, and also to develop the country's renewable energy sources such as wind power.

David Layton (1991) suggests in his article 'Values in design and technology' that value judgements are the 'engine' of design and technology. He lists the following kinds of values as being influential to design decisions:

- technical   e.g. the right materials for the job
- economic   e.g. thrifty use of resources
- aesthetic   e.g. pleasing to look at
- social   e.g. equality of the sexes and regard for the disadvantaged
- environmental   e.g. ecological benignity and the need for sustainable development
- moral   e.g. sanctity of life
- spiritual   e.g. commitment to a conception of humans an their relationship with nature.

To this list could be added cultural, political, ethical and personal values.

Consideration of such issues is of interest to children. When a class of nine year olds was studying the making of paper, the children made their own paper by recycling old newspapers. When, later, they visited a paper mill, they were anxious to discover the extent to which the firm's method of manufacture was environmentally friendly. They had anticipated defensive justifications for a non-environmentally friendly approach on the grounds of financial costs.

They were somewhat surprised therefore to discover that, not only did the manufacturer use a large proportion of recycled paper, but they also managed their own forests, planting two trees for every one which was cut down. The children were further somewhat non-plussed when their guide showed them the factory's own water treatment plant and asked them what they had done with the inky water they had disposed of in their own paper-making at school. For the paper manufacturer, environmental values were placed quite high. It clearly made good business sense to be seen as being 'green'.

The teacher of another class of nine year olds, studying space flight, was surprised at the sophistication of the children's responses when she asked them to consider what might have influenced President Kennedy's decision to develop the technology to land a man on the moon before the end of the 1960s. The encyclopaedia on a CD ROM provided them with the facts, and even an extract from Kennedy's speech, but the children were adamant that the decision had more to do with 'beating the Russians' than the desire to roll back the frontiers of knowledge.

An overview of some of the significant events in the history of technology highlights not only the way technology has advanced, but also provides some indications of the value systems which underpinned those developments.

It is argued that the earliest form of technology was epitomised by the stone tools and weapons made by our ancestors, for cutting, skinning, smashing and digging. The value judgements involved at this level of technology are mostly concerned with technical decisions – whether flint is more suitable than granite for sharp tools, and whether one type of flint will knap (break in a predictable way) when struck better than another. One has only to study the exquisitely worked quartz arrow heads from the later periods of the Stone Age to appreciate how decisions came to be made on aesthetic as well as functional qualities.

Each of the ancient civilisations contributed to developments in technology. Mathematics evolved out of the need to measure and count for taxation purposes, architectural edifices reflected power and rank rather than simply providing shelter. Sailing vessels and road networks grew out of the need to trade and administer growing empires and spheres of influence.

Many of the advances in technology disappeared with the decline of these ancient civilisations and it was not until the Middle Ages that

Western Europe began the steady climb towards what is considered to be the developed world. The relationship between prosperity, affluence and the rise of technological innovation is one which is readily apparent, though which is the precursor is open for debate.

Moving on in history one might ask, why did the Industrial Revolution occur in ninetenth century Britain? At the resource level, it was the large and readily available supplies of coal and iron ore which contributed to the rise of the industrial society. But these environmental factors were widely available in many other countries, so why should a relatively insignificant little island off the coast of the European mainland become the breeding ground for a technological revolution? The answer provides some indication of the importance of cultural, social and political factors upon the development of technology.

When, towards the end of the eighteenth century, civil unrest in India led to a drop in processed cotton imports from there and an increase in raw cotton from the Caribbean, the combination of surplus finance, a well organised financial system, a highly motivated, well-educated, open-minded entrepreneurial class, and increasing demand for goods created the climate in which new ideas for manufacture were seized upon and developed.

The need for more efficient textile manufacturing devices led to greater demand for power sources. The demands made on the new machinery gave rise to the development of the iron, steel and engineering industries. The switch from water power to steam power increased the demand for coal, which further stimulated the demand for coal mining machinery to increase efficiency and to support the excavation of deeper mines.

So, a combination of a particular political, cultural, social and financial structure, coupled with an interwoven network of increasingly sophisticated human needs, gave rise to the rapid development of technological innovation in a relatively brief period of time.

A class of seven and eight year olds, who were studying local aspects of the Industrial Revolution, were taken for a walk along the nearby Bridgewater Canal, the world's first industrial canal built by the Duke of Bridgewater to carry coal from his mines to the River Mersey. However, the children were so familiar with their environment that they hardly noticed what was around them. In a flash of inspiration, the teacher imposed a rule that they were not to take more than five steps without asking a question, no matter how trivial. Before long she and her two parent helpers were being bombarded with questions:

"Why is the water brown?"

"Why is it called the Bridgewater Canal?"

"Who made it?"

"When was it made, and why?"

"Why does that steel boat float?"

"What's making that rainbow pattern on the water?"

"How did barges get through bridges?"

"Where did the horses go at bridges?"

"Why is that brick bridge curvy and that metal bridge all square?"

"Where does the water come from?"

Back at school, the children and the teacher decided which questions could be answered by looking in books, which could be answered by trying out some experiments or making things, which questions might need to wait until they visited the museum, which might be answered by the elderly lady who was coming to talk to them about her childhood memories of living on a horse drawn canal boat, and which had no easy answer.

Among the latter category came some which were value laden including: *"Why build a canal?" "Is a canal better than a road?" "Why don't we use canals for carrying cargo now?"* With many of these, the children had to accept their own speculative answers and seek the opinions of others.

Technology: meeting human needs

Many definitions of technology refer to the satisfaction of human needs; and Maslow's (1943) proposal that needs can be ranked hierarchically has come to be seen as an important model for the analysis of human activity.

Maslow's levels of need can be summarised as:

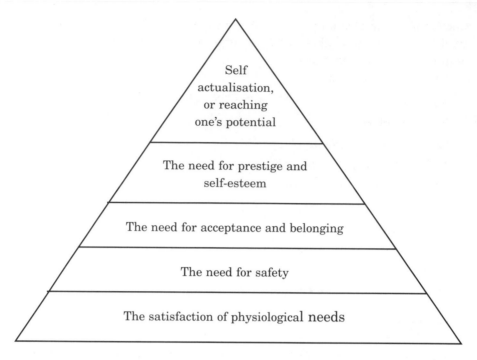

As each level of the hierarchy is reached, the technological choices become wider and more complex, and, incidentally, the potential for impact on the environment becomes greater.

In villages in rural areas of India and Africa, considerable energy is invested in installing a simple supply of water. Contrast this with the vogue for bottled water in affluent countries, where the shape of the bottle and the brand name on the label are seen by some to confer social acceptability.

To a refugee, shelter is of prime importance, and sheets of cardboard, polythene or corrugated metal will suffice in extremity. On the other hand, an architect may agonise over the shape of the finial on top of the roof of a prestigious tower block for a wealthy client.

When comparing the ancient civilisation in the Indus Valley with their own local community, a class of eight year olds in a suburban school in Britain was asked to evaluate why the buildings, clothing, tools and implements for carrying out everyday tasks were designed and made the way they were. Why for example, were the houses and streets in the Indus city of Mehenjo Daro arranged in radiating rows, while the houses on their own housing estates were more haphazardly positioned? Were the influences geographical, architectural, technological, or had it something to do with the preferences of the people? This led the children to plan their own ideal houses and housing communities with, needless to say, highly convenient leisure facilities. None of the children considered the need for services such as water or electricity. Their needs at this basic level were so adequately catered for in their daily lives that they took them for granted. Their perceived needs were far higher up Maslow's hierarchy. By working up through the hierarchy of needs, the teacher was able to focus the children's attention on what might be required for their ideal town.

One has only to consider life in different periods of history or other cultures to see the enormous contrast in the satisfaction of needs at opposite ends of Maslow's hierarchy.

Bernard Guri, an agriculturalist from Ghana, highlights an important feature of the technological choices involved when tackling needs-related problems at higher levels of Maslow's hierarchy – with greater choice should come greater responsibility.

> This is the way you live ... a throwaway life. In the Third World, we use something until it is destroyed. We use old cans to carry water; when they get a hole we patch it. You create waste. You make rubbish and pollute the environment. One day I went to a rubbish tip here in England; I saw all kinds of things which at home I could have fixed and used to furnish my house. Many of them were not even broken. They were just out of fashion. You have created advertisements to tempt you to buy things you don't need. You throw away good things to make room for them.

> Bernard Guri in *Make the Future Work* by Catherine Budgett-Meakin, 1992, p. 23

Intermediate Technology is an organisation which supports rural communities in the Third World by setting up development projects which provide technologies which are appropriate to the local needs of a community. To a community that has little or no experience of or resources for repairing machinery, a more efficient ox plough is of greater use than a tractor. For the Intermediate Technology group 'appropriate technology' is epitomised by these features:

- it is sustainable and non-violent to the environment, eco-systems and people
- it is within the economic means of a community or individual
- its manufacture is local, building on local resources, skills and ingenuity
- it enables people to earn a living and increases their ability to generate income
- it leads to self respect and increased self reliance

- it uses renewable sources of energy wherever possible
- it fits in with and is adapted to the local social and cultural environment
- it is not an end in itself but part of real development owned and controlled by the community

Technology and the environment

Ann MacGarry (1992) in her article 'Appropriate designing begins at home', argues that we in the developed world should consider the appropriateness of our technology by evaluating the extent to which it accords with these same criteria. When one considers that most of the environmental problems which beset the world – global warming, climate change, depletion of the ozone layer, acid rain, pollution, waste, dwindling energy resources – are the product of past and ongoing technological decisions made by advanced nations, then the importance of taking account of the environmental and cultural implications of technological decisions cannot be over-emphasised. The extent to which technology is the culprit, and the extent to which technology can provide solutions to environmental problems, is a discussion which is beyond the scope of this chapter, but an appreciation of the interrelationship between technology and humankind is fundamental to any study of technology, whatever the age of the children concerned.

Environmental issues are, of course, of immense interest to children and opportunities for discussion can arise in various areas of the curriculum. The following examples illustrate how children can become involved in issues relating to technology, energy sources, pollution and the disposal of waste.

After a visit to a recycling centre, the children in one primary school not only devised systems for sorting and storing the school's recyclable waste, but put an information pack together for their parents. As a result of their efforts the school was able to generate extra income from selling paper, cans and plastic bottles from the local community. The older children became so sensitive to high use of disposable items that when it came to their annual Christmas party, they voted to forego the customary use of paper plates and cups and plastic spoons and undertook to wash up the crockery and cutlery themselves with a little help from parents.

A class of ten year olds, studying homes, wanted to discover the factors which affected the temperature inside homes in different cultures. Whereas the inhabitants of homes in southern Spain were concerned with keeping their homes cool and their houses were designed accordingly, those in Britain were supposedly designed to be kept warm. By studying information on houses which were specifically designed to conserve energy, and by carrying out experiments to further their understanding of the insulating properties of different materials, the children produced their own designs for energy-conscious houses. They made model houses from a variety of materials and some lined roofs, walls and floors with a variety of insulating materials bought from the local DIY store. They then measured the effectiveness of their designs and models at conserving energy. They did this by placing a bottle of warm water in each model. A temperature sensor was placed in each bottle. This was connected to a computer via data logging equipment, which recorded the drop in temperature at set intervals over a period of time.

While taking part in a national survey of the location and healthiness of ponds, a group of ten and eleven year olds from a village primary school became concerned about the quality of water in some of their local ponds. They discovered from an environmental organisation that the nitrates in agricultural fertilisers can have a devastating effect on the ecological balance of ponds and rivers. One of the children's father was a farmer and was invited into the school to explain his farming methods. The information he provided prompted the children to write to the Ministry of Agriculture Fisheries and Food suggesting that some of the subsidies presently being paid to farmers for cutting back on food production could be used to encourage organic farming practices.

Conclusion

The resource and social factors which influence technological design decisions, the fundamental significance of value judgements, the level of sophistication of human need underlying a piece of technology, and the environmental and cultural implications of technology are intrinsic to, and inherent in all aspects of technological activity. While technological artefacts can be studied in isolation, it is only when they are placed in their human context do their designs actually have full significance. In the increasingly technological society in which we live, it is important that children are encouraged to consider such issues to help them become better informed consumers and users of technology in the future.

References

Budgett-Meakin, Catherine (1992), *Make the Future Work: Appropriate Technology: A Teacher's Guide,* Longman

Layton, David (1991), 'Values in design and technology' in Budgett-Meakin, Catherine (1992), *Make the Future Work: Appropriate Technology: A Teacher's Guide,* Longman

MacGarry, Ann (1992), 'Appropriate Designing begins at home' in Budgett-Meakin, Catherine (1992), *Make the Future Work: Appropriate Technology: A Teacher's Guide,* Longman

Maslow, A. H. (1943), 'A theory of human motivation' *Psychological Review,* 50, pp 370-96

Further reading

The following titles provide background reading for technology in general:

McCormick, R. et al (1993), *Technology for Technology Education*, Addison Wesley

Pursell, C (1993), *White Heat: People and Technology,* BBC Publications

This following volume, a companion to, *Make the Future Work,* provides more information about appropriate technology:

Carr, M (ed) (1985), *Appropriate Technology: A Reader*, Intermediate Technology Publications

Further information about Intermediate Technology, its work and its educational support materials can be obtained from: Intermediate Technology, Myson House, Railway Terrace, Rugby, CV21 3HT

The following titles provide some background reading in the development and role of Technology in education:

Benyon, J et al (ads) 1991), *Understanding Technology in Education,* Falmer

Cross, A & McCormick, R (eds) (1987), *Technology in Schools,* Open University Press

McCormick, R et al (1992), *Teaching and Learning Technology,* Addison Wesley

2 Invention

In the classroom

The process of invention and its exploitation to meet human needs and aspirations is neatly illustrated in the following project undertaken by a class of ten year olds studying 'Writing'. The activities, which the teacher had organised, were designed to develop the children's understanding of writing and writing materials through the ages, and their appreciation of how the available technology affected the way in which a particular form of writing developed. The children made their own clay tablets showing examples of wedge-shaped cuneiform script. They made paper, quill pens and their own ink from soot. They printed with printing blocks made from a range of materials and produced their own newspaper using a desktop publishing package on the computer. They researched information about the Sumerians, the Egyptians and hieroglyphics and Gutenberg's printing press, and found out at first hand how their local newspaper was printed by following through a story from a reporter's visit to the school to the newspaper's eventual publication.

Although starting with the *what*, *when* and *how* of the development of writing, the teacher also wished the children to develop some understanding of the purposes of writing, its virtues, its drawbacks, its social impact and significance – the *why*.

To address these wider aspects, she started by asking the children how they knew what life was like in Ancient Egyptian times. After the initial responses of "I saw it on a television programme" and "You told us", she was able to focus their attention on how the writers of information books and the makers of schools' television programmes gained their information, and then on to how historians and archaeologists gathered their raw data. At last, Shaun commented, "They [the Ancient Egyptians] wrote down what they did on a wall and someone read it."

A game of Chinese Whispers highlighted the accuracy and permanence of the written word as opposed to the transience of the spoken word.

Discussion of Gutenberg's invention of the printing press brought out an interesting set of social and cultural issues which surround radical innovation. The teacher drew on the children's understanding that by using a word processor, they were now able to convey their thoughts and opinions in writing to a much wider audience than previously. She related this to the impact of the invention of the printing press, before which knowledge and power had been in the hands of the very few who could read and had access to the limited number of books painstakingly written out by hand. Through some role play drama, the children came to appreciate how the intelligentsia of the day, philosophers, statesmen, churchmen, policy-makers, could only communicate their ideas directly to their immediate community. The teacher was able to emphasise how the invention of the printing press enabled a writer's thoughts and ideas to be more widely disseminated. Although beyond the scope of the children, she realised that printed books and documents allowed research to be replicated and challenged and others' views to be sought and incorporated into the development of a theory or a hypothesis. Without the printing press, it has been argued, western science and technology would not have advanced at the pace it did. It was a necessary precursor to the scientific and industrial revolution.

By emphasising the role of writing and printing in transmitting and recording events and culture and in shaping people's thinking, the teacher was helping the children to appreciate that, when studying technology, it is just as important to attend to the human implications of innovation, as to the technical aspects of an invention. This is because technological and social development are inextricably interwoven. The goal of scientific activity is the acquisition and development of knowledge and understanding, whereas the objective of technological activity is an outcome – usually the solution of a human problem.

In later chapters we will see how teachers can develop children's skills, knowledge and understanding of technological and associated scientific content. We will examine teaching and learning styles which encourage the development of problem solving strategies and how direct teaching can systematically address the development of children's knowledge and skills of materials and techniques. In this chapter we explore the wider implications of the technology curriculum.

The study of technological innovation is full of stories which children find fascinating. These examples of 'real world' technology can help children to:

- develop their own strategies for solving problems, by studying the variety of approaches adopted by inventors to solving technological problems *i.e. inventing*

- appreciate the importance of evaluation and the constantly evolving nature of technology by studying case histories of the development of new products or processes. In many situations it can be shown that an invention builds on an evaluation of previous inventions and makes use of new knowledge, materials and techniques to achieve incremental improvements. *i.e. inventions*

- appreciate the interrelationship between society and technological development by studying past, present, future and speculative innovations *i.e. innovation and society*.

Inventing

After making bread in the school's kitchen area, a class of ten and eleven year olds was asked to invent a machine which would be able to carry out the whole process automatically – from flour to loaf. The children's ideas were highly imaginative (see chapter 10). The teacher did not expect the children to implement their inventions. Like much of Leonardo da Vinci's work, their plans would remain on paper only.

When she took them to a nearby bakery to see how bread was actually manufactured, not only were the children able to follow the process through, they even made some suggestions as to how the machinery could be improved! What none of the children had predicted was the way in which, once the dough had been mixed, the entire process was continuous – each loaf in constant motion until packaged. The children's later work on conveyor belts and machines reflected their increased understanding.

When a teacher of a class of nine year olds asked them to suggest what alternative materials could be used for familiar objects if plastic had not been invented, one enterprising child suggested a wooden toothbrush with hedgehog spine bristles. The children's subsequent researches into the history of everyday objects caused a little consternation when they discovered dentures had once been made of wood, ivory or the teeth of dead soldiers.

After hearing Babette Coles' story *The Trouble with Dad*, six year old Josie designed a house-cleaning machine. Not only was it highly imaginative, but it also revealed her grasp of mechanical systems (Figure 2.1).

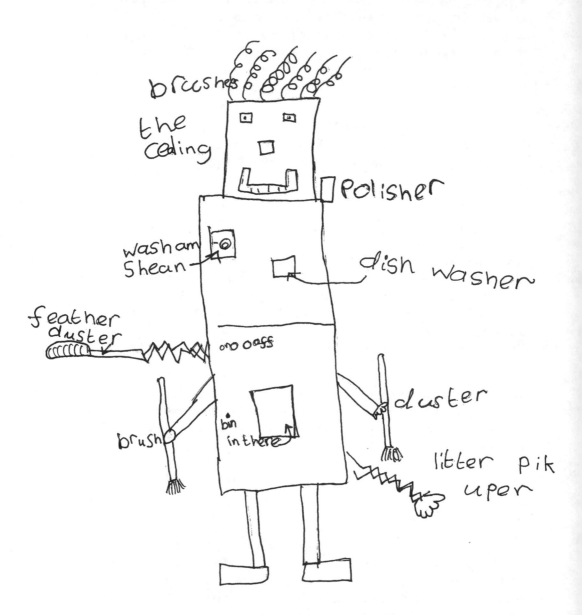

Figure 2.1 Josie's house cleaning machine

So what is the place of inventing in the Technology curriculum? Is it realistic to expect children to invent? Can we, or should we teach inventiveness? Does studying the lives and works of inventors contribute anything to our or our children's understanding?

The work of Edward de Bono on thinking, creativity and invention, though written over twenty years ago – *Technology Today* (1971), *Children Solve Problems* (1972), *Eureka! An Illustrated History of Inventions* (1974) – is still relevant, perhaps even more so with the recent upsurge in attention on technology in education. De Bono argues vigorously that young children not only can but should be encouraged to develop their imaginative, creative and inventive capabilities, and goes on to propose teaching and learning programmes to achieve this end e.g. *Teach your Child to Think* (1974), *Teaching Thinking* (1976).

De Bono suggests that studying the work of inventors and the process of invention can help us appreciate the importance of lateral thinking – approaching a problem from a completely new and original direction. The sewing machine is a prime example of the way in which lateral thinking operates because, rather than trying to replicate conventional hand-sewing techniques, Elias Howe's machine (later popularised by Isaac Singer) used two threads to produce a lock-stitch. The Wright Brothers succeeded in constructing a workable flying machine by ignoring conventional wisdom and making an inherently unstable aeroplane – necessitating a focus on the control systems required to keep it airborne.

What is encouraging for the primary school child and teacher is that many inventions came about through non-specialists identifying a specific, individual need. The pneumatic tyre, for example, resulted from a Scottish vet, John Boyd Dunlop, wanting to help his son ride his tricycle to school over rough cobblestones. Bette Nesmith Graham devised a way of covering up inaccuracies in typing by inventing a white fluid to paint over her mistakes. The demand became so great she soon found herself bottling her magic solution for friends and colleagues. Twenty years later she sold her multi-million dollar Snopake business and retired on the proceeds. Percy Shaw, a Yorkshire factory worker, realised that his propensity to follow tram lines illuminated by his car's headlamps on foggy nights might be worth extending. He invented cats' eyes.

As with Josie's house-cleaning machine, a whole host of inventions became successful because they made existing jobs easier – such as James Spangler's vacuum cleaner, later made famous by William

Henry Hoover. Some are the result of recognising marketing needs. The supermarket trolley came into being when Sylvan Goodman, an Oklahoma store owner, noticed shoppers stopped buying when their shopping baskets became full. He reasoned that if they could be given a larger basket they would spend more.

From time to time there are examples of inventions or discoveries which come about by accident or good fortune, such as William Perkin's creation of the first aniline dyes. Perkin was attempting to synthesise quinine. In the process he produced a beautiful purple liquid. Alert to the considerable interest at the time in producing a good purple dye, he sought the assistance of a firm of dyers in Perth. They tested the liquid and it proved to be just what the fashionable Victorians were looking for. William Perkin then went on to produce a range of different colours of aniline dyes. Later, in Germany, scientists started to use the dyes to stain slides. They noticed that some of the bacteria that took up the dye later died. This discovery is considerd to be an important landmark in the development of antibodies, to leading to the birth of the pharmaceutical industry.

Serendipitous invention, albeit on a different scale, does occur from time to time in the classroom, but clearly, one cannot reasonably prepare for this. What is useful, however, is an analysis of the processes many inventors employ in the realisation of their products.

Design drawings are often used by inventors, not to communicate their ideas to others, but to externalise their thoughts and test ideas. For similar reasons, an inventor might start the process of design by making a simple prototype. When Christopher Cockerell wanted to test his initial ideas about the principles of hovercraft lift he used a coffee tin and a cat-food tin bolted together. Only at a later stage did he make detailed drawings. Goodman's first ever supermarket trolley was literally a basket on a metal frame with castors attached. He may have made a rough sketch, but it is highly unlikely he would have made a detailed drawing to test his idea. On the other hand, an architect would have to make detailed drawings to communicate his ideas to prospective clients, and to those constructing the building.

A comparison of two differing approaches to the solution of the same problem can highlight the processes of invention. Although Sir Humphry Davy was credited with the invention of the miner's safety lamp, at the same time a little-known colliery engineman, George Stephenson, came up with a very similar design. Davy approached the problem of finding a means by which a flame could burn safely inside a lamp in a gas-filled mine by conducting a series of laboratory experiments to ascertain the explosive properties of the coal-mine gas methane (or fire-damp). Stephenson, on the other hand, worked on his lamp through a process of trial and improvement. Stephenson's information-gathering consisted of testing his theories and prototype lamps by descending into gaseous sections of the coal mine, in which he worked, lighting lamps and watching what happened – much to the consternation of his colleagues. The two approaches to the same problem exemplify two methodologies for practical problem-solving – the more 'scientific' approach which involves a considerable amount of initial systematic data-gathering, and the hands-on, practical approach, in which information is acquired on a need-to-know basis – only that which is required for immediate use is accumulated. In the primary school, the latter style of working tends to be adopted in order to maintain children's interest and engagement with the problem.

For children, the most valuable aspect of studying the process of inventing is the opportunity it provides for them to reflect upon their own strategies and working practices.

In many respects, the process in which children engage in practical technological activity in the classroom resembles that practised by craftspeople, who are usually involved in labour-intensive, one-off or small batch production, working with familiar materials, producing artefacts which are individualised but not necessarily technologically innovative. Making use of the experience of local craftspeople provides opportunities for children to see the entire process of invention – the design, manufacture and marketing of a product or service and the interrelationship of each stage. The ways in which the workshop, tools and materials, and working practices are organised also provide useful examples. After a visit to see a silversmith at work, the children in one junior school decided to completely reorganise their practical area to make better use of the space available.

Inventions: The story, evolution and realisation of ideas

Evolutionary studies of technology such as transport through the ages, the story of flight homes, past and present, are familiar topics in the primary classroom. However, studies of everyday items or activities – domestic appliances, dental hygiene, bread-making, writing implements – can provide useful starting points for an examination of the history of technology and invention.

The inventions which are studied need not be spectacular or epoch-making. Good use can be made of the local environment. In Chester, for example, there are four bridges across the River Dee. The history of their building provides a valuable insight into factors affecting design and the choice of materials.

The oldest bridge (now called the Old Dee Bridge), originated before medieval times and is mentioned in the Domesday Book. At first this structure was built of wood; but when the Black Prince ordered its repair in the 14th century, the decision was made to replace the wooden structure with one of stone, as the Cheshire forests were no longer extensive enough to provide sufficient affordable raw material. Stone was quarried from a sandstone outcrop adjacent to the southern end of the bridge but, owing to disagreements as to funding, the bridge took eight years to reach a satisfactory stage of completion.

Medieval masons were well practised in making use of the arch as a stable form of construction (see Chapter 5) but the seven arches of the Old Dee Bridge were of different sizes.

Figure 2.2 Old Dee Bridge

One explanation for the size variation is that each arch was funded by a different guild, and the size of the arch reflected the extent of the guild's contribution. Another more mundane suggestion is that the footings for each span were placed on the most secure parts of the river bed. The bridge not only exemplifies a stage of technological and architectural progress but provides an insight into the economics, availability of raw materials, local trade and politics of the medieval period.

In 1818, a Grand Jury meeting in Chester, noting that Chester was the gateway to Wales and Northern Ireland and that the narrow, single track medieval Old Dee Bridge was insufficient for the traffic needs of the time, called for the construction of another bridge. There were fears in the city that the suggested building of an alternative route to the north of the Chester would cut the city off from prestigious and lucrative Liverpool and Manchester to Holyhead traffic. The new bridge needed to be able to cope not only with the existing traffic, but a projected rise in traffic flow. The location of the bridge was also important in order to ensure traffic passed through the city. However, the most appropriate site provided a major constructional problem. The bridge had to be sufficiently tall for sailing boats to pass beneath to reach the Dee Mills further upstream and yet be wide enough to cope with the expected traffic flow. The city fathers were also very anxious that the bridge should be in keeping with the historic appearance of the nearby castle and the prestige of the city of Chester.

Accepted bridge technology of the day suggested an iron bridge was the best solution, owing to the length and height of span required. However, the proposed humped shape and restricted width of an iron structure failed to satisfy the design considerations of the sponsors. The engineer Isambard Kingdom Brunel, although only nineteen years of age, was consulted. His design for an arched bridge constructed from rubble, although technically advanced for its day, failed to impress the bridge committee as it was felt its appearance was not in keeping with the city's heritage. An ambitious scheme to build a single elegant arch of stone then received attention. To that date, no span of 60 metres (200 ft) had ever been constructed in stone, and there were considerable doubts as to its efficacy. The architect, Thomas Harrison, was convinced a single arch was feasible, and constructed a model to demonstrate the structural integrity and appearance of his design. After several years' deliberation, work finally commenced in 1828 and the Grosvenor Bridge completed to his design in 1832.

Figure 2.3   Grosvenor Bridge

At the time it was the world's longest unsupported stone arch and within five years, was one of the first in the world to be equipped with gas lighting. The city was clearly proud of its contribution to architectural history. It is a testament to the designer that the bridge remains the longest stone span in the UK and its width and strength is sufficient for today's traffic.

In this case, the technology which was ultimately chosen to build the bridge had more to do with the city's civic pride and prestige than the practicalities of crossing the river.

The next bridge to cross the Dee at Chester was a rather unimpressive cast iron girder railway bridge, and yet its story is significant in the history of bridge building materials. It was built in 1847 by Robert Stephenson as part of the railway link from London to Holyhead.

As bridge building developed from an art to a science, engineers came to learn more about the behaviour of materials and designs, to the extent that they could calculate the distribution of forces within a structure and more accurately predict the maximum loadings which could be placed on it. Predictions for this bridge, however, proved inadequate. The length of span of this bridge was greater than any constructed up to that time but Stephenson was confident of its strength and had calculated its expected loadings to be well within the capabilities of the materials and the design. These calculations, however, failed to take account of the weight of track

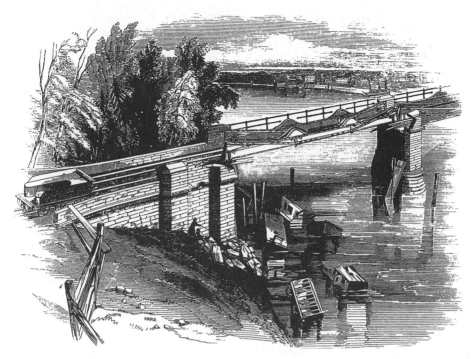

Figure 2.4 The Chester railway bridge disaster, 1847

ballast – the stone chippings on which the track is laid – and the bridge was built and tested before the full depth of ballast had been laid. When the railway line became fully operational, the depth of ballast was increased. The additional load of the first train to pass over the bridge caused it to collapse with a loss of fourteen lives. This disaster proved to be a valuable learning experience for all bridge builders, as it dramatically demonstrated the lack of tensile strength of cast iron and the importance of taking account of dynamic forces on a structure (see Chapter 5). From that time, very few railway bridges were constructed of cast iron. The story of this bridge therefore represents a minor milestone in bridge building history.

The choice of bridge building here illustrates the extent to which bridge design is dependent upon the quality of the materials used, the extent of the skills and knowledge of the designers and the need for ease of construction, in this case taking an existing design and stretching it further.

The fourth bridge to cross the Dee in Chester was a suspension bridge. Originally built during the reign of Queen Victoria, its purpose was to provide the occupants of a fashionable housing area south of the river pedestrian access to the park, riverside amenities and city centre. A suspension bridge was chosen because it looked attractive, provided sufficient clearance underneath to allow

Figure 2.5   Queen's Park Suspension Bridge, Chester

pleasure boats up river and was not too expensive (it cost £85,000). Clearly the choice of construction had as much to do with cost as efficacy, and the decision to press ahead was made despite the considerable doubts expressed in local and national newspapers as to the quality and durability of this particular design. As predicted the materials chosen (cast and wrought iron) rapidly deteriorated, leading to the bridge's replacement by one of steel in 1923.

The history of Chester's bridges represents stages in the progress of technology: each new solution to the problem of bridging a gap providing a clue as to the availability of materials the engineering know-how at the time the bridge was constructed and what society thought was important at the time – its value-system.

Innovation and society

We have already seen that the motivation for a number of inventions can be provided by immediate, individual needs. But one of the things which needs to be examined is why some inventions become very successful and others languish in obscurity for prolonged periods, or never see the light of day at all.

Why is it, for example, that Sir Clive Sinclair's attempts to produce electrically powered vehicles have met with some derision and singular lack of commercial success? Are they technologically unsound, or impracticable, or are there other factors which dictate the success or failure of a product?

For instance, why was it that the stirrup did not become popular in the West until fifteen centuries after it had been invented by the Assyrians? It clearly has nothing to do with its technological complexity, or its lack of usefulness. It was simply because no one wanted it. People took great pride in their horsemanship and were not keen on using a device which would enable even a poor rider to ride as well as an accomplished one. It was only after it became apparent that stirrups gave a cavalryman an advantage in battle that they became accepted. Social acceptance plays a great part in the success of an idea or invention.

Why was it that the native populations of the North American continent never used the wheel? Was it because it was never thought of, the need never arose, or the people decided it wasn't particularly useful? Children's toys from ancient Mexico indicate they were aware of the wheel's existence – so they must have chosen not to exploit its use.

One reason why the motor car remains the most popular form of transport, despite the deleterious effect it has upon the environment, is that few people can see any value in the alternatives. It has been suggested that if the world's oil reserves were suddenly to disappear, a viable alternative would be found within a year – hence the old adage 'necessity is the mother of invention'.

It would seem, therefore, that the process of innovation often involves a great deal more than the introduction of a new piece of technology. For something to be successful, not only does there have to be a clear need identified, but those who are going to use it need to acknowledge its usefulness to them, and those in power need to accept or encourage its use.

Innovation, the exploitation of invention, lies at the heart of present day industry and commerce. To be successful a company must harness creativity and turn it into commercial advantage. Children can be made aware of this through visits or video.

When introducing a new product, a company will normally carry out extensive market research to determine whether or not the buying public is ready for it. Occasionally clever marketing can create a demand, such as in the case of the cornflake. It succeeded where other cereal products failed, not because it was significantly better, or tastier, but because it was marketed brilliantly by the brother of the inventor, Will Keith Kellogg. Here, the technology existed, but the market didn't – an example of what is called 'technology-push', where the pressure from an innovation forces a change upon society – in this case people's eating habits, and what is considered to be healthy.

In 1902 beards were becoming less fashionable and the existing cut-throat razor was in need of revision. King Camp Gillette, a bottle-top salesman, decided that the secret of commercial success lay in providing something which would be disposable and used frequently. He came up with the razor blade. It took Gillette a great deal of effort and frustrating research to produce thin steel with the right properties, and the machinery to manufacture it, before he was able to share his idea with the world. It became a rapid success. By 1904 he had sold 12.5 million blades, and 90,000 safety razors. He had identified a market need, and developed a product to fit that need – an example of 'market-pull'. Society was ready for a change, and the technology was created to serve the change.

Attempting to predict the likely course of technological progress is fraught with difficulty. In the early days of computing, the management board of one of the world's now-leading computer manufacturers was very concerned about the future of computing. They thought it unlikely that there would ever need to be more than six computers in the world! At that point in time they could not envisage a palm-top computer, as small as two packets of soap, costing considerably less than a week's wages yet being several times more powerful than the colossal three tonne computer with which they were familiar. The phenomenal progress made with computer and micro-electronic circuitry is a symbiotic blend of market-pull and technology-push. Computer manufacturers continually develop more sophisticated devices and features for their machines and try to persuade us they are worth having (technology-push) while consumers and businesses demand more and more from the technology and put pressure on manufacturers to meet our needs (market-pull). It is not just a technology itself which is important, it is how people use it which dictates the speed and extent of its development.

In our society we have some freedom of choice: individuals can choose for whom they vote, or which products they buy, or services they support. This has an impact on what and how technologies are exploited. Ten years ago there were few if any 'environmentally-friendly' products on supermarket shelves. Consumer-demand, (market-pull) has helped place them there.

At a more immediate level, children can become involved in local issues. Why do consumers prefer one product to an alternative? To what extent are they influenced by fashion, trends, opinions and peer pressures? When they were studying bicycles as part of a larger study of local transport, the nine and ten year olds in one primary school conducted a survey of their peers and visited their local bike shop to find out what factors influenced the purchase of bicycles. Were mountain bikes really a lot better than their predecessors? Sales figures seemed to indicate they were far more popular, and yet very few of the children surveyed seemed to use them for cross-country work, which is what they were specifically designed for.

Henry Ford, a pioneering technologist, once stated that history was 'bunk'; but by examining the way in which society and technology interacted in the past, we can gain some insight into how present events might unfold.

Conclusion

In the primary school, a study of the way in which inventors have gone, or go about, the process of invention and the development of their ideas can provide a valuable opportunity for children (and teachers) to broaden their historical and technological knowledge and examine the implications of innovation. By careful selection of contexts, most of which can be familiar and immediate, children can become aware of the interplay between social and cultural development and technology.

Many everyday inventions have an interesting history and provide an insight into a society's awareness of scientific knowledge and its effects. The technology-related decisions of the past have affected our present and the choices individuals make in the present will affect the world of the future. The better informed children are, the wiser their decision-making will be.

References

Cole, B. (1985), *The Trouble with Dad*, Picture Lions

de Bono, E (1971), *Technology Today*, Penguin

de Bono, E (1972), *Children Solve Problems,* Penguin

de Bono, E (1974), *Eureka! An Illustrated History of Inventions*, Thames and Hudson de Bono, E (1974), *Teach your Child How to Think,* Penguin

de Bono, E (1974), *Teaching Thinking,* Penguin

Further Reading

The following books provide interesting information about the invention of many familiar items.

Baren, Maurice (1992), *How it All Began: The Stories Behind Those Famous Names,* Smith Settle

Davison, Michael (ed.) (1992), *Everyday Life Through the Ages,* Reader's Digest

Ellacott, S.E. (1969), *A History of the Everyday Things in England, Vol. V,* Batsford

Giscard d'Estaing,Valerie-Anne (ed.) (1990), *The Book of Inventions and Discoveries,* MacDonald Queen Anne Press

Hooper, Meredith (1992), *I for Invention: Stories about Everyday Inventions,* Pan MacMillan/Piccolo

Kane, Joseph (1981), *Famous First Facts,* H W Wilson

McCormick, Robert, Newey, Charles & Sparkes, John (1993), *Technology for Technology Education,* Addison Wesley/Open University

Quennell, Marjorie & Quennell, C.H.B (1918), *A History of the Everyday Things in England, Vols. I–IV,* Batsford

Robertson, Patrick (1986), *The Shell Book of Firsts,* Treasure Press

Taylor, & Lambert, M (1979), *The Mechanical World,* Macdonald Educational,

Tibballs, Geoff. (1994), *The Guinness Book of Innovations,* Guinness Publishing

3 Children as technologists

As has been seen in the previous chapters, technology is the means by which we attempt to satisfy human needs and wants. The role of technologists is to analyse problems and, drawing on scientific and technical knowledge and understanding, to devise solutions which meet the requirements of particular situations.

If technology is to do with the solution of practical problems, then what are the implications of this for organising technological activities in the classroom? How can we help children become technologists? First we must set the scene to allow children to identify their needs themselves. Then they can set about developing ideas on how these needs may be met, and finally apply all their scientific and technical skills to make products which satisfy these needs. In this way we will foster a genuinely technological approach.

The poddalump trap

Technology has been described as problem solving in a context. With children, the context provides not only the reason for technological activity but also the motivation.

> And then, just as they came to the Six Pine Trees, Pooh looked round to see that nobody else was listening, and said in a very solemn voice:
>
> "Piglet, I have decided something."
>
> "What have you decided, Pooh?"
>
> "I have decided to catch a Heffalump."
>
> Pooh nodded his head several times as he said this, and waited for Piglet to say "How?" or "Pooh, you couldn't!" or something helpful of that sort, but Piglet said nothing. The fact was that Piglet was wishing that he had thought about it first.
>
> "I shall do it," said Pooh, after waiting a little longer, "by means of a trap. And it must be a Cunning Trap, so you will have to help me, Piglet."
>
> from *Winnie the Pooh* by A. A. Milne

All of us have our own ideas about how best to motivate the children we are working with in order to spark an enthusiastic response. But imagine that somewhere in the far reaches of your classroom there lives a near cousin of the Heffalump, a poddalump – a shy but amiable creature about the size of a large mouse. Little is known about the poddalump, due to its retiring nature, but it might be possible to capture one to find out more if an effective and humane trap could be constructed.

The designing and making of poddalump traps can capture the imagination of children of all ages in the primary school and the story of Pooh's Heffalump trap is only one of the ways in which a challenge of this nature might be presented to them.

The six 'snapshots' which follow give brief insights into children of different ages at work as technologists. Building on the scientific and technical knowledge with which they are familiar, they bring different solutions to design and make a humane trap to capture a poddalump.

Laura (aged six) used a cardboard box as the basic structure for her trap. A front-opening flap provided an entrance and a string was attached to the flap to allow it to be raised and lowered. She put a hook on top of the box to tie the string to when she realised that she would have to sit holding the string to keep the entrance flap open. Laura was quite happy with this design in spite of the obvious drawback that she would still have to be continually on hand in order to close the flap when the poddalump had gone in. She was more concerned with making the inside of the trap comfortable, putting in cotton wool bedding and a ball for the poddalump to play with.

Another six year old (Sam) used a long narrow box with transparent plastic panels for the basic structure. These panels were to allow you to see the poddalump when it was inside. The hinged flap at the end of the box was propped up with a piece of wood which could be knocked away with a stick when the poddalump had gone in. Later Sam decided to tie a piece of string to the stick to pull it away rather than knocking it down, explaining that it would be less frightening for the creature inside.

Both these traps were made from ready-made boxes, but as children become more skilled and knowledgeable, they are able to construct traps from a wider range of materials and also incorporate more sophisticated operating devices, which require the harnessing and control of an energy source to do the work required.

Energy

Energy can come in a variety of forms:

animal or human power	e.g. pulling, pedalling, hand-turning
natural power	e.g. sun, water or wind
potential energy	e.g. stretched elastic band, raised weight
electrical energy	e.g. battery, photocell
chemical energy	e.g. burning coal, gas or oil

Usually the primary energy from one of these sources is converted into mechanical energy to make a machine or device work or operate. For instance, an electric motor converts electrical energy into turning mechanical energy. Usually this mechanical energy then needs to be modified to suit the device it is driving. Speed, power and direction of motion can be altered by a series of mechanisms such as gears and pulleys. These are called transmission systems. In addition, the driving mechanisms (energy source and transmission) must be controlled. In the simplest case this will be an on/off switch but it may include speed control or steering devices. More elaborate control systems use sensors to detect a change in the environment and then make the device operate automatically in response to the change. For example, photocells or pressure switches are used to control automatic doors. An important type of control is feedback control, which is often used to maintain a constant level of temperature, speed, or pressure. If the speed of a machine falls below a set level, this will be detected by a built-in device and a message relayed to increase the speed again by adjusting the rate at which energy is supplied and transmitted.

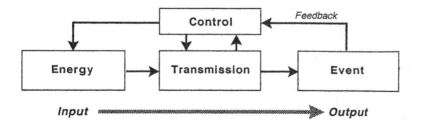

Figure 3.1 Diagram of transmission and control of energy

The following manually-powered trap was designed and made by a group of eight year-olds.

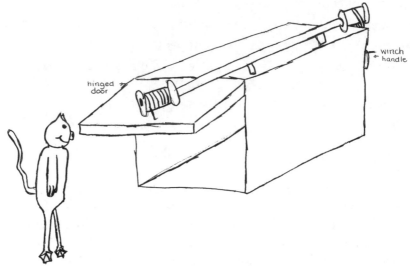

Figure 3.2   The manual poddalump trap

It was constructed from thin sheets of wood cut to size and joined at the edges using a glue gun. This proved to be more challenging than they had envisaged, as the pieces of wood needed to be measured and cut very accurately to fit together properly. The door was wound up manually with the winch, a cotton reel with string wound round it. When the poddalump entered the trap, the winch was quickly unwound, closing the door and trapping the poddalump inside. In this case the energy came from a child winding and unwinding the handle. The transmission of this energy was through the winch, the string and the pulley system to the hinged door, and the control was provided by the child observing the poddalump entering the trap and operating the mechanism at the appropriate time.

Although this solution showed construction skills, the solution to the poddalump problem had the same drawback as Laura's trap: the operator needed to be constantly on hand.

Another solution to the poddalump problem, this time devised by a group of ten year olds, used gravitational energy and a simple linkage mechanism.

The trap was made from lengths of square section wood cut to size and joined at the corners with cardboard triangles. The children had used this technique on previous occasions and were able to construct mitred corners which produced a neater finish. Each framework was covered with pieces of corrugated plastic sheeting, cut with a craft knife and attached to the framework using a glue gun (figure 3.3).

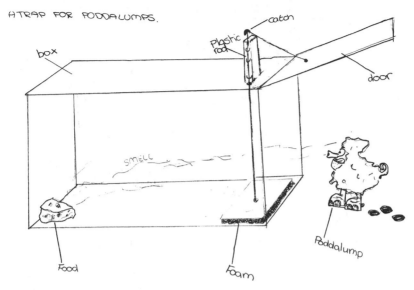

Figure 3.3   The mechanical poddalump trap

As can be seen, once the doorway had been raised and the mechanism set, there was no need for an operator to remain present. As the poddalump entered the trap, it stepped on the 'trigger', releasing the door, which swung shut through gravity. The energy was provided by gravity and the control came through the linkage mechanism which transmitted the poddalump's weight to the door catch. Once released, the door hinge converted stored gravitational energy into a swinging motion to close the doorway.

The principal disadvantage which the children identified with this trap, was that the poddalump might be frightened or injured by the door swinging shut. It was also realised that another catch would have to be fitted to keep the door closed, otherwise the poddalump could push it open again with his nose or bottom!

Another solution employed electro-mechanics and gravity (figure 3.4).

Like the previous trap, the frame was made from lengths of square section wood cut to size and joined at the corners with cardboard triangles. Initially the children chose to cover the frame with wood but found cutting this to size too difficult and resorted to using thick card instead. The top of the trap was covered with a sheet of transparent plastic, giving a bird's eye view of any captured poddalump.

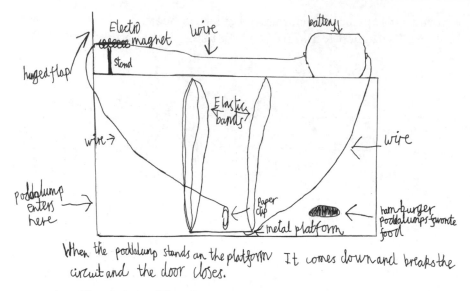

The following labels appear in the figure:

Electro magnet · wire · battery · hinged flap · stand · Electric bands · wire → · wire · poddalump enters here → · Paper clip · metal platform · hamburger poddalumps favourite food

When the poddalump stands on the platform it comes down and breaks the circuit and the door closes.

Figure 3.4   The electro-mechanical poddalump trap

Again as in the previous trap, the door was held open, but this time an electro-magnet was used as a 'catch'. Thin insulated wire was wrapped around a nail and electricity passed through the wire, magnetising the nail. When the poddalump entered the trap, its foot pressed a lever attached to a home-made switch. This switch turned off the current to the electro-magnet and the nail lost its magnetic attraction, releasing the door. A small permanent magnet held the door closed. The energy for the operation of the trap again came from gravity, but the control of the mechanism was electrical.

The eleven year old children who had made this trap thought it was highly ingenious and were reluctant to fault it. The teacher, however, felt it necessary to point out that the continuous use of electricity to hold open the door could be a drawback – especially as electro-magnets use a great deal of current and will drain a small battery very quickly.

The most sophisticated solution to the poddalump problem involved the use of an electric motor and gearing (figure 3.5).

When an unfortunate poddalump entered this trap, he unwittingly switched on an electric motor, which, with much clanking and whirring, slowly and quite gracefully, pulled the door closed. The motor converted electrical energy into fast rotational motion which was slowed down by a series of gears to turn the winch and close the door.

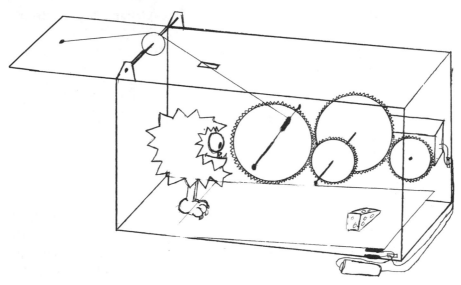

Figure 3.5 The motorised poddalump trap

After the children had constructed the trap, they realised that someone needed to be present to turn off the motor once the door had closed, otherwise the winch would keep pulling on the door. At their teacher's suggestion they fitted a micro-switch to turn off the power to the motor once the door was shut.

This activity combined an element of construction with the need for some kind of operating device. The children's solutions to the problem reflected their abilities to design and make, and their levels of knowledge and understanding to choose suitable materials for a given task, and to apply a range of skills for cutting, shaping and joining and constructing mechanisms and electrical circuits. The fact that children, when encouraged to find their own solutions to problems, tend to use ideas which they really understand and value, gives us as teachers good guidance on possible next steps. Clearly some of the children were ready for some more advanced construction techniques; others would have benefited from the introduction of simple switches; and for some of the older children the use of computer control could have added another dimension to the problem (e.g. enabled them only to catch poddalumps over a certain weight, or to devise a trap which alerted the trapper when a poddalump had been captured).

What these snapshots do not give us is an insight into the way in which the children approached the problem. They do however give some indication of the children's abilities to make reasoned decisions, and also of the importance of the context in capturing the children's interest and involvement and in motivating them to seek a solution to the problem. If a context is carefully chosen to provide opportunities to integrate prior experience with new opportunities, the children will respond in an imaginative way to the challenge, building on skills and knowledge they already have and, in some cases, learning new ones on the task.

Problem solving

Our aim as teachers is to develop children's competence and confidence to tackle problems independently and to equip them with the skills and strategies to solve problems themselves. But how can this be fostered in children's design and technology activities in the classroom?

First, the importance of identifying contexts which provide problems of significance for children is of fundamental importance. Second, if we interpret the children's responses, however naive and limited, as a stage in their learning process, we begin to see the opportunities for developing competence and for fostering independence. Children cannot become expert technological problem solvers overnight. They need time and a series of experiences to develop their skills and knowledge. At first the problems which they encounter might be fairly limited in scope.

Put simply, a problem can be defined as a goal with an obstacle. You want or need something, but something else is stopping you achieving that objective.

The goal for the children was to devise a humane way of catching a poddalump. The obstacle was finding a realisable means of achieving this objective. Every child was able to solve the problem, but the level of sophistication of their solutions depended greatly on the extent of their experiences. Like the River Dee bridge builders, the technological knowledge and skills available to them were a major factor influencing their decisions.

There are many models describing the problem solving situation, but the cyclic model (figure 3.6) is probably a version with which most people are familiar.

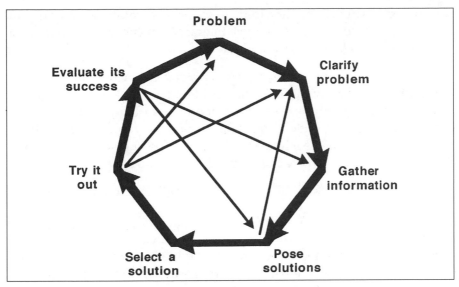

Figure 3.6 The problem solving cycle

The solution of a problem – whatever the context – requires the application of past experience, skills, knowledge and a degree of self-confidence. Not only the skills and knowledge of the appropriate *subject matter*, but skills in, and knowledge of, *strategies* for tackling similar problems or problems in general. A skilled electronics expert would have a greater range of options for solving the poddalump trap problem than someone who has little knowledge of electricity. But a person who has just returned from five years of self-sufficiency on a desert island will probably be better equipped with practical skills in seeking solutions than someone who has always relied on others to solve problems for them.

Research studies have shown that while most primary children are often well-equipped with knowledge and skills related to subject-matter, they are less likely to be proficient in strategic skills – the thinking required for independent problem solving. Problem solving skills can be developed in any curriculum area (e.g. see Robert Fisher's *Problem Solving in Primary Schools* (1987)), but design and technology lends itself particularly to the acquisition, practice and application of these important capabilities.

Young or inexperienced problem solvers will often rush for an immediate solution to a problem without considering alternatives. They may have little relevant knowledge of suitable technological solutions, or only a limited understanding of associated skills, techniques or the uses of appropriate materials. This is the constant dilemma facing teachers who are beginning work in design and technology – they want the children to solve practical problems, but realise the children have not yet acquired sufficient knowledge or experience to achieve this unaided.

As with any activity, there are times when a teacher may need to intervene considerably in a child's problem solving – especially if the child has a low tolerance of frustration or insufficient experience to solve the problem unaided. Problem solving is by no means a hands-off situation for the teacher. Problems can be solved by a group, a class committee or by teacher and child together.

> What a child can do with assistance today she will be able to do by herself tomorrow
>
> Vygotsky, *Mind in Society,* 1978

Lev Vygotsky, for one, places great emphasis on the role of other people in children's learning. He stresses the importance of nurturing the growth of a child's independence by maintaining a balance between *timely* intervention and *appropriate* non-interference by the teacher. The teacher's role is crucial in terms of providing opportunities, support, guidance, resources and, where necessary, direct instruction or assistance. The greatest difficulty can come in recognising when it is more appropriate to hold back and allow the child to learn from her own mistakes. This is where the art of structured progressive questioning comes to the fore:

"*Why are you doing that?*"

"*That's interesting, can you tell me how it works?*"

"*What will happen if ...?*"

"*Is there another way to ...?*"

"*Have you thought of ...?*

"*Have you tried ...?*"

"*Here's my idea, would you like to try it?*"

From the initial open-ended enquiry, the questions become increasingly focused to the point that the teacher feels the child is in a position to continue independently. By explaining to the teacher, the child is reinforcing her own understanding, probing a solution's efficacy, and predicting an outcome. In addition, the teacher is providing a model for children to follow, as these questions are just those which the children should ultimately be asking of themselves to become fully independent problem solvers.

The electro-mechanical trap described earlier came about partly from the children's ideas and partly through the suggestions of the teacher. This raises another issue. Should subject related skills, knowledge and techniques be taught directly, or acquired in the context of a problem? The professional judgement of the teacher will determine this. There are occasions when children can be shown a technique, or the novel use of a familiar material whilst attempting to solve a particular problem – on a 'need to know' basis. But there are also times when it is more appropriate to show a group, or a whole class, a method or the use of a tool – particularly with technologically inexperienced children. Children cannot be expected to generate solutions to technological problems if they have little or no knowledge of suitable approaches. As they gain experience they will begin to discover their own techniques – then they can teach each other and even the teacher.

> In the beginnings, zest and inventiveness are more important than exactness or finish, but no course should satisfy either teacher or child that does not eventually lead to livelier realism, better design and more precision in the finished product.
>
> Board of Education, 1937

Although this was written in 1937, it is no less true today. But to this can be added the centrality of problem solving to Design and Technology. Without this, children cannot act as true technologists.

References

Board of Education (1937), *Handbook of Suggestions for Teachers,* HMSO

Fisher, R (ed) (1987), *Problem Solving in Primary Schools,* Basil Blackwell

Vygotsky, L (1978), *Mind in Society,* Harvard University Press

Further Reading

There are several books currently available which provide information related to the development of children's skills and understanding when working in Design and Technology in the Primary School.

Jarvis, T (1993), *Teaching Design and Technology in the Primary School*, Routledge

Tickle, L (ed), *Design and Technology in Primary School Classrooms,* Falmer

4   Designing

"Let's make something that nobody's ever made before and call it a name that nobody's ever used before!"

Sarah (aged 7)

Introduction

Young children progress very quickly as they make sense of their world and try to exert an influence over it – to communicate with their native culture, to mould new words, to fashion new shapes, to design and colour. Indeed much of that sense is made through the actions of young hands. Our desire to design has very early beginnings and it exists in us all.

Take Louise, for example, just six and desperate to design a book. The following monologue took place at about the same speed as it will take you to read it.

> "I'll fold them and write in them then I'll staple them. There's some felt tips for when I need them, but I'm going to draw the pictures first.
>
> Now, what'll this be about? A fairy ... or a fairy ... or a fairy, or a heart, or a Prince and Princess?
>
> Not a heart.
>
> I think I'll do it about a princess and a fairy! I'm going to do the princess sitting on her bed talking to the fairy.
>
> Right here's her leg ..."

Her vocalised thought allows us to capture the sort of decision making that is tacit in adults. It is true that the intended audience for her story is probably the same as for her thoughts – herself – but harnessing her desire to create, and coming to understand the process that she employs, is necessary if we are to assist with its development.

Figure 4.1 The fairy and the princess

There are many models of the design process, and by familiarising ourselves with them and reflecting on them, we are in a better position to respond effectively to the 'windows on thinking', which children display when engaged in design and make activities.

The process

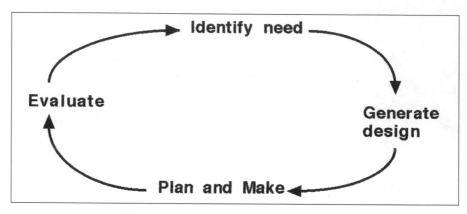

Figure 4.2   A design process model

This basic model (figure 4.2) of the design process has many inadequacies. Consider how well it fits with what has been described in the short extract earlier. Some of Louise's decisions are made as mentally she evaluates the effect of alternatives or the practicalities of her own suggestions as she thinks about making her book and planning the order of its assembly. While she is certainly in the early stages of a larger process, there is also a micro level of the process as she adjusts her thinking in smaller feedback loops. As the project unfolds on the macro level, a range of shorter cycle, micro design processes manifest themselves as hurricanes, tornadoes or momentary eddies that last for a second or two. The model then assumes another dimension of complexity (figure 4.3).

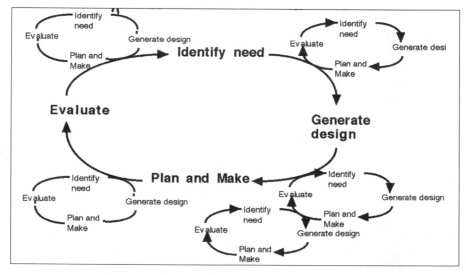

Figure 4.3   Another design process model

The reality of children's early designing is that, as materials and fastenings and skills are put to the test, the practical work is honing the original design ideas, and other decisions are tested as practical activity forces a rethink of ideas. The interplay of practical activity and thought is what makes design technology such a valuable part of the development of young children. The model below (figure 4.4), devised by the Assessment of Performance Unit, describes the potential for progression that is possible as practical activity develops thought and reflection, which, in turn, leads to further refined practice.

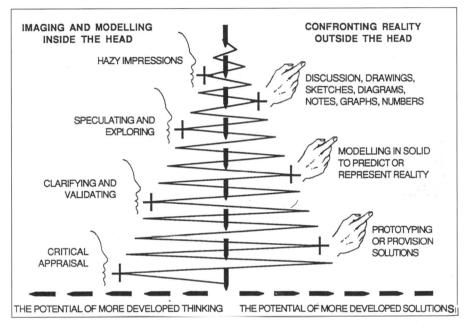

Figure 4.4   The APU model of interaction between mind and hand

But what about professional designers? Where do they begin? One professional product designer describes the following key stages in the process of realising a new product (figure 4.5).

Within this approach there are many features resonant with children's processes which can help us to develop ideas and practical skills. If we see practical work as an integral part of children's thinking as opposed to the culmination of thought, then room must be made for experimentation and evaluation in our own planning of classroom activities. A careful balance of activities is called for which expands the range of what is possible, with design opportunities to use and develop skills and knowledge and understanding as we plan children's work.

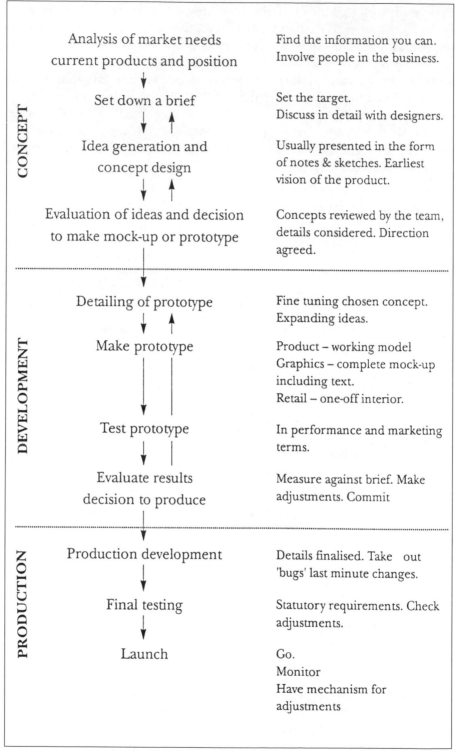

Figure 4.5   The Raffo process: realising a new product

Design is fundamental to the task which faces us every day. As we plan and organise the physical context for learning, design the work based on evaluation of the individual needs of the children in our care, and evaluate the effectiveness of our design through our interaction with the children, we are immersed in aspects of the design process.

Windows on thinking

In the example which follows, the class teacher was attempting to respond to the need to integrate practical work with thinking, as opposed to viewing it as the culmination of thought. Within the context of a broader topic on 'Transport', her class of seven and eight year olds was working on a challenge to design and construct a vehicle to make the perilous journey across the classroom from 'table one' to the door. By setting a specific challenge, the teacher aimed to identify variations in the processes and techniques adopted by the children, consider reasons for those differences and also identify burgeoning understanding. Having initially planned and and set up an activity based on her current knowledge of the children, she then helped them to evaluate their progress and decide on appropriate ways forward. A crucial part of her role in this process was listening and watching to glean the necessary information about where the children were in terms of understanding and skills.

At the drawing board ...

The children, working in small groups, started to design their vehicles on paper and identify materials that would be required. While some of the children tried to articulate very precise visual images on the paper, others were more aware of a structure necessary to maintain the position of the four wheels. A few, very pragmatically, designed around available resources.

Nazmin's group's design (figure 4.6) fell into the category which could be described as 'fantastic'.

Their drawings resembled actual vehicles that they had seen, and included detail like the rear-view mirror, but no mention was made of the materials to be used. These children could be considered to be 'dreamers' focusing almost exclusively on the concept with little thought of the practicalities of construction.

Heather's group adopted a somewhat 'potentially drastic' approach when designing their vehicle (Figure 4.7)

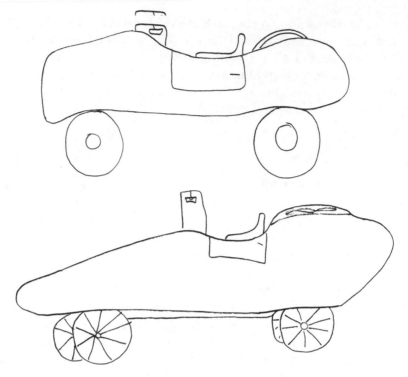

Figure 4.6 Nazmin's group's designs

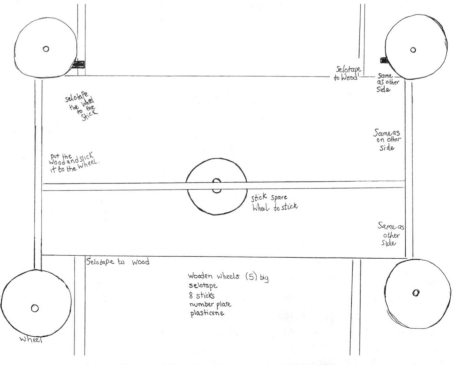

Figure 4.7 Heather's group's design

Although the drawing considered the materials to be used in construction, the basic 'H' design betrayed a lack of experience with either the materials, structures, or fastening techniques. The drawing showed narrow dowel butted and stuck and described wheels taped to axles. The children's insistence on a roll of Sellotape suggested that this form of fastening had proved to be a panacea in the past.

Peter's group, however, put forward a more 'realistic' design (figure 4.8).

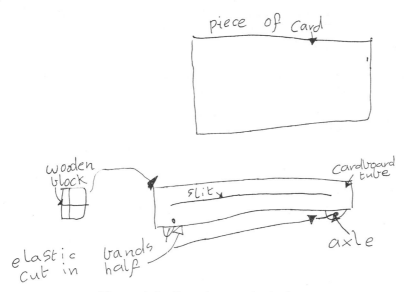

Figure 4.8   Peter's group's design

Their drawing offered diagrammatic representation of the structure with notes explaining the materials used. Although they were not the most inventive or creative, they demonstrated an understanding of the characteristics of the materials suggested. The children had drawn the components separately showing how they intended to assemble the parts, but not the actual joining technique, although a slit indicated the join of the card to the tube chassis. The problems that they encountered with their idea of rubber band suspension will be discussed shortly.

Beyond the 'window' on the children's thinking that a pencil and paper exercise provides, there are important skills in graphic representation to be developed. The first stages of design drawing and modelling are to communicate to others what the end result of the exercise is going to look like and how it will perform. Initial inadequacies of the two-dimensional drawings of young designers are helped with rough assembly of components and/or construction kits. The recognition that one view of an object is not sufficient develops with the child's ability to decentre. The recognition that some important aspect of their model is not visible from a single perspective is an important step in a child's development.

Interestingly the professional designer introduces details of scale and dimension to drawings only after the prototype has been made. The audience for professional designs is often a manufacturer, possibly on the other side of the world. The process of representing prototype models by drawings of different elevations and three dimensional sketches for manufacture by other people, demonstrates the power of carefully labelled drawing to communicate ideas.

In a class of eleven year olds, the teacher simulated this process by pairing groups in the class. The children were making dancing marionettes. Each group was asked to make drawings of their model at various stages of completion, as well as of the finished design, while it was still in front of them. They were then asked to add measurements and pass the drawings to their partner group on the other side of the classroom to recreate their design. The children carefully refined their designs as each group had to both give and interpret information and they were swift to identify gaps in the drawings that they were receiving.

Looking at other people's designs is very valuable. Trying to understand other people's ideas from their drawings and plans is as fertile to design as reading is to language development. Using drawings of buildings and articles which are familiar to children helps to develop their ability to translate drawings into objects and vice versa. Plans of the school building and contemporary patents can be a fruitful source. Searches at the Patent Office are expensive but regional science and technology libraries have archives of patents which they will search and copy.

A teacher of a class of ten year olds was explaining the special ability of drawing to communicate ideas and objects across centuries. Using a book of the drawings of Leonardo da Vinci, she asked groups to use construction kits to help to explain to the rest of the class how the drawings might have worked. The children were then encouraged to add their own instructions to clarify the parts of the drawings which 'we can't quite see ...' . By considering the difficulties involved when interpreting pictures drawn by someone not available for questioning, the children recognised the need for clarity and precision in their own drawing.

While there is plenty that we can learn from analysing children's designs, the benefit of our learning needs to be translated into action through our response to each group or individual's differing needs.

With Nazmin's group, no amount of designing on paper was going to develop their understanding of the properties of materials and ways of joining and fastening them. Further concrete exploration was needed before they could proceed. Simply allowing them to try to follow their ill-defined plans was likely to result in disappointment. Since a crucial part of the challenge was to make a buggy that moved, their teacher decided to focus their attention on the wheels and set up directed activities based on different ways of joining axles to wheels to allow rotation and investigating the different materials which could be used.

The teacher felt that Heather's group had a sufficient idea to make a start. The task would challenge them, but, with sensitive intervention, it offered considerable scope for learning. Too much teacher participation could make the potential difficulties 'disappear' and, at the same time, remove the learning opportunity. A lack of support at the right time, allowing the group to experience too much frustration, however, would be similarly destructive to the development of the group's technological capability.

Peter's group seemed to have a clear idea of where they were going and, apart from suggesting that they put some measurements on their drawing, the teacher decided to leave them to pursue the task.

On the assembly line ...

As the designs started to take on a concrete form, Heather and her team quickly hit the snags in their design. How could they join two sticks at right angles? Amy knew that the wood was too thin for nails. Heather suggested that they could cut a bit of wood out of each stick and slot them together. But they didn't pursue this – perhaps because they weren't too sure how to go about it. Laura then remembered that they had used an elastic band to lash sticks together when they had been making kites earlier in the year. They seized on this idea and applied elastic band lashing to the stick chassis (figure 4.9).

Although not ideal, they could now continue their construction along the lines set out in their design.

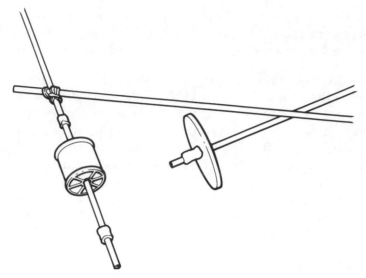

Figure 4.9   Heather's Chassis

The challenge of making it run in a straight line was just around the corner! On test runs the car was found to veer off course. Heather was quick to straighten the elastic band joint but recurrence ultimately led to a remaking of the joint by cutting the dowel to correct the wheel alignment and make it run in a straight line (figure 4.10).

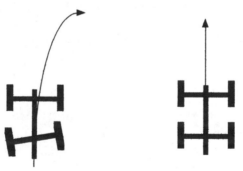

Figure 4.10   Heather's H construction

The 'H' construction of this vehicle needed to be strengthened to ensure that the two axles were parallel to each other.

Peter's group, who knew something about suspension from watching rally driving, had some insider information on the cardboard tube market! They began to construct their version of independent suspension quite accurately. By fastening the axles to the cardboard tube chassis with an elastic material (pieces of rubber band), they were aiming to allow a degree of movement (figure 4.11).

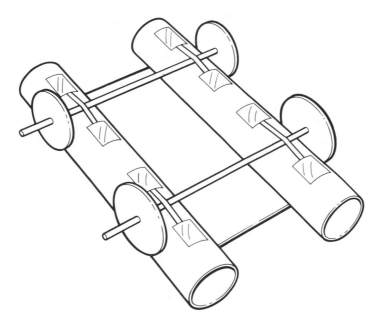

Figure 4.11   Peter's Chassis (upside down showing suspension)

Suspension

This is the system which absorbs the jolting of the terrain in most land-based vehicles. It is based on elastic materials or systems – i.e. ones capable of retaining their original shape when no longer pushed or pulled.

Springs are traditionally used but there are many types of waste plastic as well as rubber and elastic products which will perform this function in models:

Extension springs are used in prams and spring balances. Rubber bands and elastic can be used to stretch and spring back in a similar way.

Compression springs are the type traditionally found in biros. Sponge, balloons and some foams can be used for this purpose.

Although they understood the elastic properties of a rubber band, they did not understand that this property could only be exploited under tension. Their design therefore did not take this into account but, as it would be easily rectifiable, the teacher encouraged the children to continue, test their design and find out the problem for themselves. They did and came to her for help. She drew their attention to the properties of the rubber band and the need for it to be extended for their design to function as planned. Two solutions were discussed. The first was to turn the vehicle upside down and use larger wheels. By doing this, the chassis would be suspended underneath the axles and so extend the rubber band. The second involved inserting pieces of foam between the axles and the chassis, achieving a degree of suspension by compressing the material. In an ideal world, the children would have tested to find out the most satisfactory way of solving the problem, but they were satisfied with the degree of success which was achieved by turning the system upside down and using a larger wheel, and were happy to leave the design there.

Nazmin's group had been encouraged to focus on the problem of making their car roll. They had learned quite a bit from the directed activity and now appreciated that when attaching the wheel to the axle, either the wheel or axle (or both) needed to be free to rotate.

Having been given a simple card chassis, they were now having difficulty with their chosen technique for fastening wheels on to axles with plasticine. They had had some experience of using beads as a type of bearing and wanted their wheels to turn freely on a fixed axle. Fixing a bead either side of the wheel with some plasticine was not allowing the wheel to move. To enable the wheel and bead to spin, the children needed to replace the plasticine with some plastic tubing (figure 4.12).

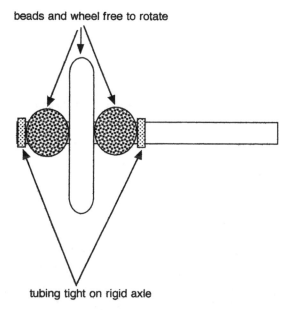

beads and wheel free to rotate

tubing tight on rigid axle

Figure 4.12 Nazmin's wheel fixed in place with beads and plastic tubing

Road test

By now, with tests and challenges well under way, the children were embarking on final evaluations, and the teacher was identifying aspects for future attention.

Heather felt that the roof of their car would have been better if it had been made of bent cardboard, "so that the wind goes over the top of the car and makes the car go a lot faster." Clearly she knew something about aerodynamics.

What could her teacher do for her? Simple air-tunnel experiments with a hair drier evaluated different designs. Using masking tape as a temporary fixing, a curved cardboard body was attached to the chassis. The car was then put on the starting line of a test grid marked out on the floor a measured distance from the hair drier. By recording the distance that the vehicle was blown, different bodies were evaluated for their resistance to wind. The shorter the distance that the vehicle was blown from the start line, the more effective the design of the body in allowing the air around it.

Amy justified sticking her wheels with Sellotape, not glue, "because if we stuck it with glue it would take a long time to set." She is telling the teacher about her experience, her criteria and possibly what she thinks of the classroom organisation. Time is obviously a factor in our calculations, but, where possible, we need to allow for more time-consuming approaches if the children are going to be able to evaluate the benefits offered by some lengthier procedures, in this case fastening techniques.

In addition, as Amy's group had shied away from using tools to join wood, the teacher needed to know whether or not this was because of a lack of the appropriate skills.

Although Nazmin's group's car (figure 4.13) did not look like the original design, the children were very pleased that it was rolling well. They were given the task of drawing the final version of the car and then asked to add one or two features from their original design which they would like to be able to add to future models. This resulted in a more realistic design, which provided an example for future work. In addition, it gave the teacher an indication of which aspects could be the focus for attention by this group, at a later date.

Peter's group had problems with their car not running straight. They quickly traced this to their advanced suspension system. The slackness in the system presented itself as both the problem and the temporary solution, as minor adjustments could easily be made to

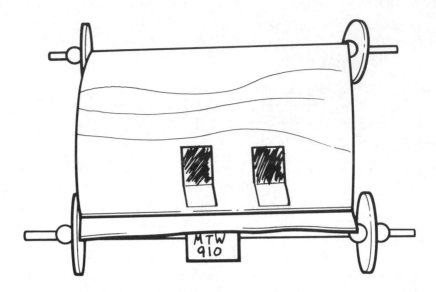

Figure 4.13   Nazmin's group's car

the alignment of the axles. These adjustments were only of a temporary nature, but discussions about possible solutions led to identification of the cause of the problem as the suspension system. The design which allowed the body of the vehicle to move independently of the axles, also allowed the axles to twist out of line. Initially the only solutions involved dispensing with the suspension system. But a visit to the staff car park identified the trailing arm solution on a Mini which like a hinge allows movement but keeps the axle straight.

This activity shows the continuous interplay of designing, making and evaluating. The considerable differences between the groups was very apparent to the teacher and it provided more information about particular strengths, weaknesses and interests, which she could build on when planning future work in technology.

Developing children's designing skills

To give the impression that design is a process that is wholly creative, fuelled by empirical discovery, with no place for following instructions or learning from a vantage point 'on the shoulders of others' would be foolish. The stories of designs and designers make a valuable contribution to the development of children's understanding of design (see Chapter 2). It is important, however, that we encourage children to see instructions as someone else's design, in the larger process described above, and not reduce practical focussed tasks to mindless activity.

It is hardly surprising that most children, given the limited range of experience on which they have to draw, initially have difficulty translating their enthusiastic designs into realistic proposals. This can be compounded by our asking for designs on paper before any practical making is permitted. Asking children to outline their ideas both verbally and in model or prototype form presents them with a real audience to question and advise about suggested materials and techniques. This process has the dual advantage of identifying practical investigations that may be carried out prior to formulating a written design, and providing an opportunity to show the children how their ideas can be communicated in design proposal form. At first young designers tend to be unsure about the appearance and practicalities of their designs but, as their experience in design and technology develops, they become more able to communicate their ideas effectively. They learn to give reasons for their choices and plan the sequence of the making process, as shown in this set of instructions for making a plaster plaque (figure 4.14).

The teacher's role in ensuring that children continue to think about their designs during the making process is crucial. Since children are often more comfortable designing 'on the model', children persuaded to commit designs to paper, unconvinced of the need for them, will often produce a detailed drawing of the object and not refer to it at all during the making process. There must be evident benefits of thinking things through on paper for the child. The usefulness and value of design drawings can be emphasised to children by displaying and keeping them in class, books or folders, after they have been used, for future reference by all the children.

Time spent understanding and developing children's thought processes as they design will help the quality of their work and the support that we can offer.

Figure 4.14   Louise's design idea and story board

Further Reading

These titles provide more general information on design:

Morrison, J & Twyford, J (1991), *Design Capability and Awareness,* Longman

Papanek, V (1985), *Design for the Real World,* Thames and Hudson

NSEAD (1995), *Designs we live by,* National Society for Education in Art and Design

These books provide more specific information about the role of Design in Technology Education:

Department of Education and Science (1991), *The Teaching and Learning of Design and Technology,* HMSO

Kimble, R et al (1991), *The Assessment of Performance in Design and Technology,* HMSO

5 Making with materials – structures

Introduction

From their earliest days, babies and small children adopt a tactile approach as they explore the world around them. We adults often behave in a similar way as we walk around a department store or do-it-yourself centre. We pick up an object and run our fingers over it, exploring the properties of the materials from which the object is made, examining how it has been put together. The question we are probably asking ourselves is, "Will this do what I want it to do?" The choices we eventually make are based on many factors, including cost and aesthetic considerations, but suitability for purpose, in terms of strength, durability, flexibility, texture and weight, will also have been very important.

Adults make choices of this kind by calling upon prior experience. We know whether a particular type of wallpaper will be likely to rip when it gets wet, if a certain kind of plastic work surface will stand up to harsh treatment in the kitchen, or a certain construction of suitcase is robust enough to withstand the harsh treatment at the airport. Children, with their more limited experience of the world, are not in such a rich position to make choices. Some of the materials offered to children in design and technology activities may well be unfamiliar to them, and they need time to explore and investigate the materials to see what they will and will not do, and find ways of joining and fastening them together. Without this period of exploration, it is probably unreasonable to expect children to make appropriate choices when they put together a design brief.

Take for example, the construction of a simple box buggy. When six year old Jake constructed this, he chose to use a card shoe box lid, a wooden axle and wooden wheels (figure 5.1). For him, these were familiar materials.

Figure 5.1 Jake's box buggy

On the other hand, eight year old Zoe decided to use card, dowel, square section wood, plastic sheeting, wooden wheels and plastic tubing, as these were part of her experience.

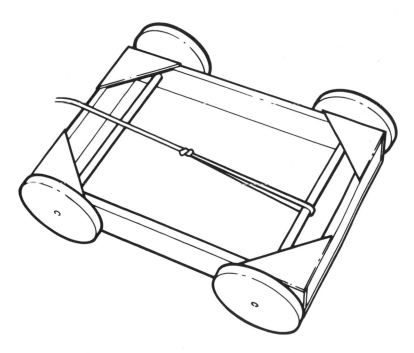

Figure 5.2 Zoe's more sophisticated box buggy

The skills Jake required were limited. He used a saw to cut the dowel axle, and a hole punch for the axle holes. When Zoe made her own box structure, she applied more advanced joining techniques, using tabs to reinforce corners and card gussets to re-inforce axle supports.

Materials

The greater the range of experiences with materials provided for children, the more choices they will have when attempting to solve technological problems. The following chart lists a range of materials most commonly seen in use in primary classrooms and highlights some of the principal properties of these materials, ways of joining and fastening them, tools to use with them and some ways in which they have been used.

Materials	Properties / features	Ways of joining and fastening	Tools	Classroom uses
Paper / card	• Flexible • Easy to use • Readily available • Cheap • Familiar to the children	• Gluing • Taping • Stapling • Pinning • Sewing • Folding • Slotting	• Hands (tearing) • Scissors • Craft knife • Stapler • Needle and thread • Hole punch	• Box structures • Cladding for frame structures (e.g. walls for half-timbered house model)
Balsa wood (very soft wood, used mostly for model making)	• Lightweight • Easy to cut and shape • Readily available from educational suppliers and craft shops	• Gluing • Slotting • Pinning • Bolting	• Craft knife • Hacksaw • Shaper saw • Hand drill • File	• Frame structures • Box structures • Cladding (e.g. sides of a model wind mill)

continued...

Materials	Properties / features	Ways of joining and fastening	Tools	Classroom uses
Stripwood (softwood in narrow cross sections (e.g. 8mm x 8 mm)	• Strong • Easy to saw • Easy to join • Readily available from educational suppliers • Relatively cheap	• Gluing • Taping • Stapling • Binding • Slotting • Pinning • Bolting	• Hacksaw • Shaper saw • Craft knife (with caution) • Mitre block • Hand drill • File • Rasp	• Frame structures (e.g. towers of a suspension bridge)
Dowel (stripwood which is round in cross section)	• Readily available from educational suppliers, craft shops and DIY stores • Relatively cheap	• Gluing • Slotting	• Hacksaw • Shaper saw • Craft knife (with caution) • Pencil sharpener • File	• Axles • Pegs and pins for fixed and flexible joints • Struts and ties for frame structures (e.g. axles for a box buggy)
Plywood (laminations of wood veneer – the grain of each layer alternates in direction)	• Tough • Strong • Thin • Relatively easy to cut and shape • Available from most DIY shops in a range of thicknesses • Expensive	• Gluing • Taping • Slotting • Pinning • Bolting	• Craft knife • Panel saw • Fretsaw • Shaper saw • Hand drill • Battery drill • Rasp	• Medium sized box structures • Cladding for large frame structures • Shaped components (e.g. linkages)

continued...

Materials	Properties / features	Ways of joining and fastening	Tools	Classroom uses
Polythene (e.g. reclaimed washing-up bottles)	• Tough • Flexible • Easy to cut • Difficult to glue • Free	• Gluing (with difficulty) • Taping • Slotting • Bolting	• Scissors • Shears • Craft knife • Hacksaw • Shaper saw • Hole punch • Hand drill	• Cladding or small box structures • Small shaped components (e.g. straps for holding down electric motor)
Polystyrene (e.g. ceiling tiles)	• Soft • Rigid • Weak • Light-weight • Relatively cheap	• Gluing (with appropriate adhesive) • Slotting • Pinning (for temporary joins)	• Scissors • Craft knife • Fretsaw • Hot wire shaper • Shaper saw	• Light-weight box structures • Aircraft or boats • Light-weight cladding for frame structures (e.g. walls of a model stone-built house)
Corriflute or Correx (plastic laminated sheet made in a similar way to corrugated card – sometimes used for temporary street signs or advertising boards – e.g. estate agents)	• Tough • Rigid or flexible • Strong • Easy to cut • Available from educational suppliers	• Gluing (with appropriate adhesive) • Slotting • Pinning • Bolting	• Craft knife • Hacksaw • Fretsaw • Shaper saw • Hole punch • Hand drill	• Small or medium sized box structures • Cladding for frame structures • Shaped components (e.g. sides for model truck)

continued...

Materials	Properties / features	Ways of joining and fastening	Tools	Classroom uses
Plastazote (similar to compressed (latex) foam rubber)	• Flexible • Mouldable (with hot water) • Easy to cut and shape • Light-weight	• Gluing (with appropriate adhesive) • Slotting • Pinning • Bolting	• Craft knife • Scissors • Shears • Hole punch	• Small or medium sized box structures • Cladding for frame structures • Shaped or moulded components (e.g. hands for puppets)
Textiles	• Flexible • Strong • Easy to cut • Can be free if reclaimed fabrics are used • Familiar	• Gluing • Taping • Stapling • Pinning • Sewing • Weaving • Felting • Knitting	• Hands (tearing) • Scissors • Craft knife • Stapler • Needle and thread • Hole punch • Looms • Drop spindles • Carders	• Garments • Cladding for frame structures • Moulded or sculpted shapes (if combined with a stiffener such as starch or plaster) (e.g. model horses for model carts)
Papier maché	• Mouldable • Can be readily shaped • Very messy • Very cheap (or free)	• Gluing • Bonding • Screwing	• Hands • Hand drill (when hardened)	• Moulded shapes (e.g. landscapes)

continued...

Materials	Properties / features	Ways of joining and fastening	Tools	Classroom uses
Plaster	• Mouldable • Strong • Can be readily shaped • Fairly cheap • Very messy	• Gluing • Bonding • Screwing	• Hands (moulding) • Chisel or scriber (for sculpting) • Hand drill (when hardened)	• Moulded shapes • Stiffening fabric for structures (e.g. simulated rock faces)
Clay	• Mouldable • Strong • Can be readily shaped	• Gluing • Bonding • Screwing	• Hands • Scriber • Hand drill (when fired)	• Moulded or sculpted shapes, such as creatures • Small box structures (e.g. model houses)
Food	• Very familiar • Wide ranging in type and properties	• Mixing, blending and combining	• Hands • Whisks, knives etc	• Edible items

But how do children accumulate knowledge of materials and working techniques? Sometimes it is necessary to introduce children *en masse* to particular materials or techniques.

When two classes of ten and eleven year olds decided to mount a fashion show in two weeks' time for the rest of their school and parents, there were some in the school who were more than a little sceptical. However, the children knew that the costumes and the decorations for the hall were going to be made entirely from paper and card. The first two sessions were spent experimenting with techniques. With the assistance of some 'borrowed' college students, the children crumpled, tore, wove, folded, pleated, sprayed, scrunched, flattened, ironed, plaited and laminated paper and card until they had developed a repertoire of techniques. They discovered that the appearance and texture of paper could be altered to create some quite unexpected results. They also discovered that paper comes in a range of thicknesses and types – each with differing properties.

Armed with their knowledge of the properties and working characteristics of paper, groups of children set about designing and making outfits for their 'volunteer' models, working to such themes as 'Seasons', 'Night' and 'Space'. The costumes were highly imaginative; some were influenced by fashion magazines, some by historical influences and others were pure flights of fancy.

While the costumes evolved, other children were designing the catwalk, lighting effects and selecting appropriate music for the themes. The final event was recorded on video by enthusiastic parents.

At other times the context may be set, but allow for a much wider range in the use of materials, enabling children to apply previous knowledge in new situations and requiring the teacher to respond to children's needs on an individual or group basis.

When a class of nine and ten year olds decided to create their own pirate museum, each child or group chose an artefact they wanted to contribute. Two life-sized ship's cannon, made from card tubes, softwood frames with corrugated card and plastic wheels, were positioned either side of the door. A relief map of Madagascar was made from papier maché on a thick plywood base. A life sized silhouette of Blackbeard, wielding a plastic and hardboard cutlass, was made from plywood and clothed in fabric. A cutaway model of a pirate cutter was constructed from stripwood, balsa wood and card. And a brace of flintlock pistols fashioned from softwood, metal piping and recycled polythene was hung from the wall.

These children had already developed confidence and skill with a range of materials and techniques before tackling this major task. Many applied prior knowledge, while there were some who needed to be taught techniques on a need-to-know basis when they encountered problems with the realisation of their ideas. Ruth and Suzie's original design for Blackbeard specified corriflute for the model's support structure. The teacher realised this would probably be insufficiently rigid to support the heavy fabric they intended to use, and introduced them to plywood.

Joining and fastening

But knowledge of the properties and working characteristics are not enough. At some point children need to learn how to join materials and components together.

When Mark was making one of the pistols for the pirate display described earlier, he discovered a way of attaching his metal water-pipe gun barrel to the wooden stock by scrutinising a drawing and making polythene hooped straps from a recycled toothpaste tube. He devised a new fastening technique through his own problem solving (figure 5.3).

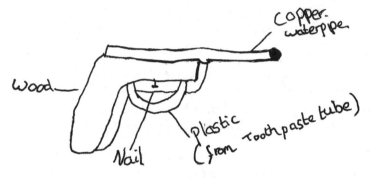

Figure 5.3   Mark's pirate pistol

Charley, on the other hand, could not find a satisfactory way of attaching his pivoting trigger mechanism to his pistol, and so the teacher had to show him how to drill a pilot hole for a woodscrew, and use washers to allow free movement (figure 5.4). He was introduced to a new technique through direct instruction on a need-to-know basis.

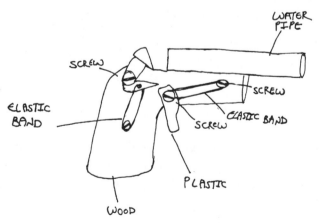

Figure 5.4   Charlie's pirate pistol

Some focused practical tasks can be devised to develop children's knowledge and skills on a particular occasion while also providing a bank of techniques for future reference. For example, Karen and her group were given a range of materials and components including fabric, card, plastic, wire, string, paper fasteners, pipe cleaners, etc. and asked to find as many ways of joining them together as they could and to display their results on a corriflute board. For half an hour they worked enthusiastically filling their boards with ideas, before explaining their techniques to the rest of the class. The boards became a permanent fixture in the classroom, with other children adding new techniques at a later date.

The chart earlier in the chapter made general reference to a range of joining techniques. The method chosen, however, is dependent upon the materials to be joined, the type of joint required, and the permanent nature of the joint. The appropriateness of the joining technique selected and the care with which it is executed affects the quality of the end product. Children's appreciation and competence in these areas only comes through first-hand experience.

Gluing

Adhesives provide a means of permanently joining materials or components. Nowadays there is an extensive range of glues, solutions and adhesives suitable for use in the classroom. This chart details some of the more familiar adhesives used in schools.

Adhesive	Type	Suitable materials	Applications	Comments
Cold water paste **Wallpaper pastes**	Starch or cellulose paste	Paper or lightweight absorbent materials	Paper lamination or papier mache	Can soak through and spoil the finish of some materials *Note:* Most wallpaper pastes now contain fungicide, so should be used under supervision

continued...

Adhesive	Type	Suitable materials	Applications	Comments
Glues and gums (e.g. Gloy, vegetable glue, etc.)	'Natural' glues	Paper and card	Suitable for lightweight joins.	Worth testing these before using them, to find their stickability
PVA adhesives (e.g. Marvin Medium, Bostik Wood-working adhesive, School Glue, etc.)	PVA resin	Paper Card Cardboard Wood Fabric Most absorbent materials	Most – from small scale card models to large wood-working projects	Water-based white adhesive which dries hard and clear or slightly opaque. N.B. only some are washable once dry
Copydex	Rubber-based adhesive	Fabric Card String (absorbent, flexible materials)	Mostly used for fabrics or situations where flexibility is a requirement	Retains its flexibility when set
Evostik Impact 2 Evostik Safe 80	Contact adhesive	Fabric Card Leather Glass or porcelain	Useful for joining different materials together	Retains some flexibility – these are non-solvent contact adhesives
Hot glue guns	Hot melt glues	Most things	Instant bonding	Not allowed in primary schools by some LEAs. There are now low temperature guns available

continued…

Adhesive	Type	Suitable materials	Applications	Comments
Bostik clear adhesive	Clear general purpose adhesive	Fabric Card Leather Glass or porcelain	Useful for joining different materials together, where appearance could be marred by glue	Retains some flexibility – contains solvents, so should only be used under supervision
Balsa cement	Cellulose cement	Balsa wood Stripwood card	Mostly used for balsa models	Sets hard, does not have a long shelf life. Contains solvents so should only be used under supervision

Adhesives have advantages over other forms of joining in that they do not usually require the materials to be altered. Some forms of joining (e.g. drilling) can weaken the material, as when a nail splits wood. Modern adhesives are very powerful. In some cases e.g. the use of PVA to join wood, the adhesive bonding is stronger than the surrounding material to which it is attached.

Other joining techniques

Most glues provide a permanent or semi-permanent join. Temporary fixing techniques, however, are important particularly if a model or device is a prototype and needs to be modified or dismantled. Some temporary and semi-permanent joining techniques are described in the following chart.

Techniques	Components	Suitable materials	Applications	Comments
Pinning	Pins, nails, drawing pins	Fabric, paper, card, wood	Temporary joins (e.g. holding fabric while sewing)	Wood should only be pinned to keep alignment while glue sets
Sewing	Needles and thread	Fabric, paper, card, pliable plastics, leather	Demountable joins (e.g. sewing, then unpicking a seam)	
Tying or binding	Threads and string	Fabric, stripwood, straws, card	Temporary or demountable joints (e.g. a puppet's limbs)	Puppets' limbs can also be linked by loops of thread to make movable joints
Wiring	Steel or copper wire, paper clips	Card, wood, plastic, metal	Temporary or semi-permanent joints (e.g. fixing the sails to a windmill to allow for adjustment)	Some early aircraft had their wooden structure wired together before strong glues were developed
Taping	Sellotape, masking tape, carpet tape etc.	Paper, card, straws, fabric, stripwood, plastic	Temporary or fixed joins (depending on the type of tape used) (e.g. building towers from rolled newspaper)	Masking tape is easier to use than sellotape, and will accept some paints

Techniques	Components	Suitable materials	Applications	Comments
Riveting	Plastic rivets, paper fasteners, paper binders, pop rivets	Card, plastic sheet, wood sheet, metal sheet	Temporary, fixed or movable joints (e.g. joints in linkages)	Rivets and riveting tools are available from most educational suppliers
Screwing	Woodscrews, chipboard screws, self-tapping screws	Wood and some plastics	Demountable joints (e.g. joints for a collapsible puppet theatre)	Drilling a pilot hole in wood help to prevent splitting
Bolting	Nuts and bolts	Any sheet material, wood strip, metal	Demountable joints (e.g. a prototype test model)	Available from most DIY shops and some educational suppliers

Structures

Just as an understanding of the properties of materials and ways of joining and fastening them is fundamental to technological construction in the classroom, so is an understanding of structures. A mechanism needs some sort of structure to support its components; a model vehicle will require some sort of chassis (frame) or a carcass (shell) for the axles and wheels. Whatever technological activity children engage in, they need to make some sort of structure at some point. But structures can also be studied in their own right; and some understanding of the forces which are acting on and in structures, while not essential, does help a constructor make rational decisions as to where, how and why particular structural components could or should be placed. The following activities show a number of different ways employed by teachers to develop children's understanding of this aspect.

Types of structure

When studying the houses in their village, ten and eleven year olds were asked by their teacher to build models of some houses to help them understand the way in which they had been constructed. A seventeenth century cottage took the attention of a group of boys and, with the help of some illustrations in text books, their field sketches and photos, they set about producing a scale model. They chose to use stripwood for the framework, joined with hot glue. Although the result was not quite an accurate representation, the model builders quickly realised which of the timbers of the framework were load bearing and which were acting as cross bracing. By filling the gaps with corrugated card, glued in place with PVA, they also realised the hogging or wattle and daub between the timbers of the actual house was merely a filler and did not contribute significantly to the strength of its structure, although it did improve its rigidity.

A group of girls, who chose to model a Georgian house, cut the walls from large sheets of corrugated card (recycled from electrical appliance packaging), joined with masking tape and PVA reinforcement card gussets. The structure of their house was provided by the walls. They soon appreciated that the addition of internal walls and floors contributed to the rigidity of their structure because the model wobbled less and less with the addition of each new internal wall or floor.

Through their studies and modelling, the children had identified the two types of structures – *frame* and *shell* structures.

Frame structures and shell structures

The boys' half-timbered house is an example of a *frame* structure – the wooden framework distributes the forces (weight of the roof etc.) to support the structure. The walls of the Georgian house provides a *shell* to distribute the forces.

Most animal bodies are examples of frame structures, with an internal skeleton (endoskeleton) of bones to provide support. Insect bodies, on the other hand, are, in the main, shell structures with a hard outside supportive layer (exoskeleton).

Forces in structures

Constructing towers out of building bricks, or trying to make structures out of playing cards, help children appreciate that successful structures are those which resist or make use of forces to maintain their stability. As the tower or card castle becomes taller, the increased forces from the weight of materials place stresses on the lower parts of the structure. When the tower's centre of gravity swings outside the base, or when the downward force from the card castle causes one of the lower cards to slip, the structure collapses.

Children often become confused about forces by making the assumption that forces only operate when something moves. When situations are static or in a state of equilibrium, they reason, there are no forces present. Technological activities provide a wealth of opportunities for these partial conceptions or misconceptions to be confronted and challenged.

When a teacher set a challenge for her eight year olds to build the strongest platform they could from Artstraws, her prime purpose was to focus the children's attention on the effect of the forces present in their structures. She tried to encourage the children to look closely at what happened when the towers collapsed under destructive forces (increased loading on the tower). Each platform had to be 30 cm high and be wide enough at the top to support a set of circular 'weights'. Each group of children was provided with an equal number of straws and the same length of masking tape. Once completed, they sketched the results and were asked to predict which tower they thought would be the strongest and where each tower would be most likely to fail when the weights were progressively laid on top of the tower.

Some towers collapsed because the masking taped joints came apart but, as anticipated, with most of the towers the legs buckled first. The designs of the most successful towers were analysed and, using the information they had gathered, the children repeated the task - to improve upon their first ideas. This time, some children reasoned that if they used all their straws in bundles to make extra-thick legs, their towers would be stronger than those which 'wasted' straws with cross-bracing. Others realised the midpoints of the straw legs were the weakest parts, and included some cross-members to try to prevent buckling. Intuitively, they were attempting to redistribute the forces acting at the weakest parts of their towers (figure 5.5).

As the teacher tested each tower to destruction, she focused the children's attention on the effects the loads were having upon the frame members in each tower, describing the way the forces were being 'shared out'. Much to the surprise of many of the class, the most successful tower was one with apparently spindly legs, but a triangulated framework which directed the forces to the base of the tower.

Figure 5.5   Tower designs by eight year olds

Compression and Tension

Two principal forces act on and in structures – compression and tension. Compression is a pushing force, whereas tension is a pulling force. In the children's towers, most of the forces present were compressive. The load was exerting a downwards force, while the ground was balancing this by exerting an equal force upwards. Thus the legs were being compressed.

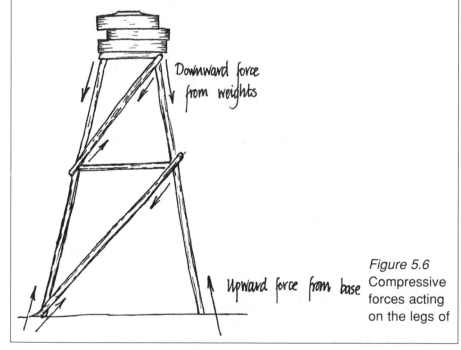

Downward force from weights

Upward force from base

Figure 5.6
Compressive forces acting on the legs of

Some of the horizontal cross-members were under tension. If a leg tried to bow outwards, the horizontal member would transfer this to the other leg which is also trying to bow outwards. The two outward forces would counteract each other. The cross-member is being pulled outwards at each end and is therefore under tension.

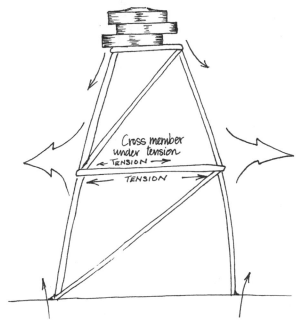

Figure 5.7 Tensile forces acting on the cross-members in a tower as the legs bow outwards

Provided the forces balance each other, the structure remains stable. Collapse occurs when the forces are no longer balanced.

The groups went on to build a third tower each, to an agreed design based on the most successful tower. This time the width of the base of each tower varied by a prescribed amount. The children (and teacher) wanted to discover the optimum design for a straw-built tower.

Figure 5.8 was their conclusion. You might like to challenge their results by carrying out your own investigations.

One incidental piece of learning which occurred with this activity enabled the teacher to introduce the concept of dynamic forces. One of the groups protested loudly when, instead of the weight being placed gently on top of their tower, it was dropped from a slight distance above. They argued that a dropped weight was 'heavier' than one placed gently. In the discussion which followed, the teacher

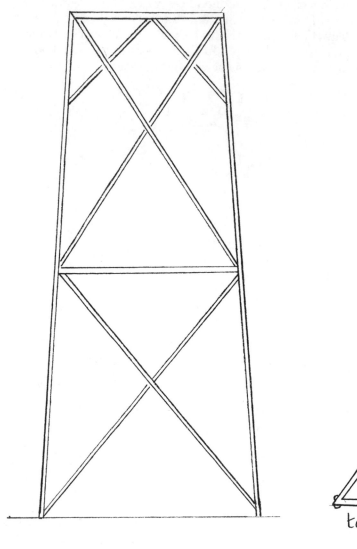

top

Our best tower is made
from three sides like this.
to make a triangle.
Each leg is made of two straws.

Patrick

Figure 5.8 The best tower design

was able to demonstrate the increase in force when a mass is propelled into a object, rather than being gently pushed, by asking one of the children try knocking a nail into a piece of wood with a pin hammer firstly by tapping gently, then by tapping hard and finally by hammering as hard as possible. Repeating the procedure with a heavier hammer helped emphasise the effect.

Static and dynamic forces

The *static forces* acting on and in a structure usually arise from the materials from which the structure is made. The mass of materials used to build a house exerts a static force upon various parts of a house. If you have ever wondered whether the bricks at the base of the walls of your house will ever collapse under the weight of all those above them, it was once calculated that it would require a tower at least 2 km tall before the static forces in the tower would destroy the bricks at the base.

Dynamic forces are principally those external forces which act at different points on a structure. The mass of a car passing over a bridge exerts a dynamic force, as does the wind blowing against a tree.

To stop a car quickly, you need to press hard on the brake pedal. To slow it gently, you press lightly on the brake pedal. The less time taken to stop an object, the more force is required. When the weight was dropped on to the straw-built tower, the tower tried to stop the weight instantaneously – requiring a great deal of force. Whereas, when the weight was placed gently on the tower, the time taken to slow the weight down, which was moving more slowly anyway, was far greater, so far less force was required. Hence, dynamic forces, depending upon the speed, direction and time taken to stop them, can have more devastating effects than static forces.

Model bridge building is another valuable activity for exploring forces in structures. Bridges have to resist a number of external dynamic forces – a river's current pushing against a bridge's supports, the wind pushing against the towers of a suspension bridge, the weight of traffic passing over it. Different designs of bridges distribute the forces acting on and in them in different ways.

In Chapter 2, we saw how a study of local bridges can focus attention on the social, cultural, political, economic and environmental implications of technology. A study of bridge design can similarly be used to highlight the ways in which a design problem can lead to several different engineering solutions – in this case, how can the river be crossed?

Main types of bridge design

Beam bridges

A beam of wood, stone, concrete or metal is placed across the void and supported at each end. The forces produced by the beam's own weight and loading placed on the beam are counterbalanced by the upthrust from the abutments beneath the end of the beam. The weakest part of a beam bridge is its middle.

Figure 5.9   Beam bridge

Cantilever bridges

Either single or double cantilever, the bridge acts as a form of see-saw to distribute the forces.

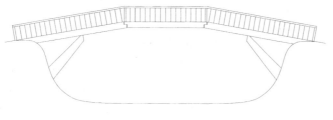

Figure 5.10
Double
cantilever bridge

Arch bridges

Whereas the Greeks relied on columns and beams, the Romans exploited the strength of the arch in their buildings and bridges. The forces in an arch are transferred to the foundations at the base of the arch.

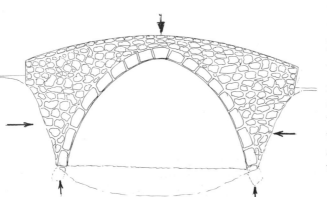

Figure 5.11   Arch bridge

Suspension bridges

The cables, which must be firmly anchored to the ground at each end of the bridge, support the deck of the bridge by transferring tensile forces to the anchor points.

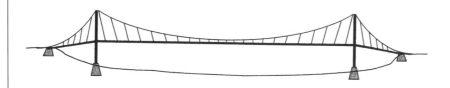

Figure 5.12   Suspension bridge

After a visit to sketch and photograph local river and canal bridges, a group of nine and ten year olds were set a challenge to bridge a metre-wide gap between two tables. Their teacher imposed a few design constraints on the 'civil engineering groups' tendering for contract. The bridge needed to:

• look attractive to both road and river/canal users

• support a 1 kg mass being pulled across in a model truck

• be self supporting (i.e. not fixed to the tables)

The contract was to be awarded to the cheapest tender meeting the above specifications. The children were also provided with a list of materials with nominal costs e.g.

thread	1p per metre
string	3p per metre
thin card	8p per A4 sheet / 36 p per A1 sheet
8mm stripwood	23p per piece

Of the eight bridges constructed, three were beam bridges, four were suspension bridges and there was one type of arch bridge - similar to the Sydney Harbour Bridge with the arch rising above the road and the road suspended beneath. Two bridges failed the strength test, one beam and the arch. This left two beam bridges and the four suspension bridges in line for being 'awarded the contract'. The suspension bridges had considerable difficulty in counterbalancing the loadings. But by judicious use of plasticine and a strategically placed book all passed the test. The cheapest bridge to meet the requirements, however, was the minimalist suspension bridge (figure 5.13).

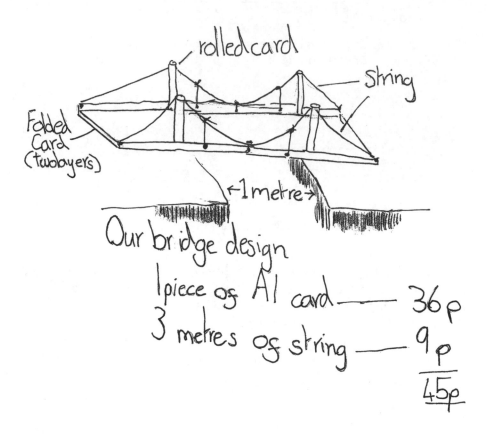

Figure 5.13 The winning bridge

The children's engagement with the activity seemed to be heightened by the contest, and comparing their solutions with those of the other groups focused their attention on structural design and the performance of various bridge designs.

Conclusion

This chapter has tried to show how, through a combination of focused practical tasks and design-and-make activities, children can gain knowledge and experience of materials and their properties, and can come to appreciate and develop fabrication techniques for basic structures. Although it is not essential to fully understand the stresses operating on and within structures, some analysis of how, where and why a structure fails can provide an insight into the forces which structural components must resist and distribute. This not only helps the children with their model making but also heightens their appreciation of the design implications of structures in their surroundings.

Further Reading

The following titles provide some background information on structures and construction techniques:

Gordon, J.E. (1985), *Structures, or why things don't fall down,* Penguin

McCormick, R et al (1993), *Technology for Technology Education,* Addison Wesley

Time Life (1992) *Structures,* Time Life Books

6 Making with levers and linkages, pneumatics and hydraulics

Making things move

Children enjoy making things that move. Five year olds using construction kits will often add wheels to their model – even if it happens to be a house! Older children may well become frustrated when they start making a model and realise they do not possess the skills required to construct the working mechanism of their design. But mechanical models do not always require gears, motors, pulleys and complex gadgetry. This chapter looks at ways in which working models and devices can be constructed relatively easily using levers and linkages, and pneumatics and hydraulics. These two approaches have the additional advantage of being relatively inexpensive to resource in the classroom.

Levers and linkages

Use of levers and linkages in our everyday lives

A good way to start work with levers and linkages for children of all ages is to examine and investigate the application of lever and linkage mechanisms in every day situations.

A quick look around, either indoors or outside, will reveal many examples of the use of levers and linkages in our everyday lives. In the home we use levers in scissors, door handles, 'squeegee' floor mops, suitcase catches, folding baby buggies, deck chairs and sun loungers. Levers and linkages also form parts of the mechanisms used in windscreen wipers, typewriters, pianos and the brakes on bicycles.

continued ...

Levers

A lever is simply a rigid bar, or other structure, which can rotate around a fixed point. The point of rotation is called the *fulcrum* or *pivot*. Levers are useful because they allow you to amplify movement or move a large load with only a little input force e.g. removing the lid from a tin using the handle of a spoon, throwing a rock a large distance.

The input force is called the *effort* and the output force is known as the *load*.

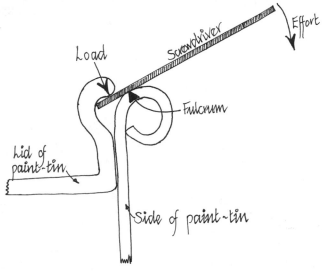

Figure 6.1
Prising the lid off
a tin of paint with
a lever

Kinds of levers

There are three kinds of levers: first, second and third class levers.

In first class levers the pivot is in the middle, the input force is at one end and the output force at the other end. An example of a first class lever is a playground see-saw.

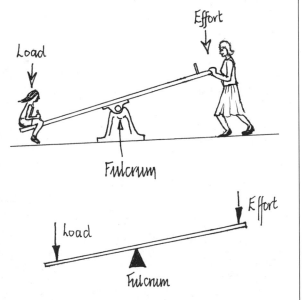

Figure 6.2   See-saw

continued ...

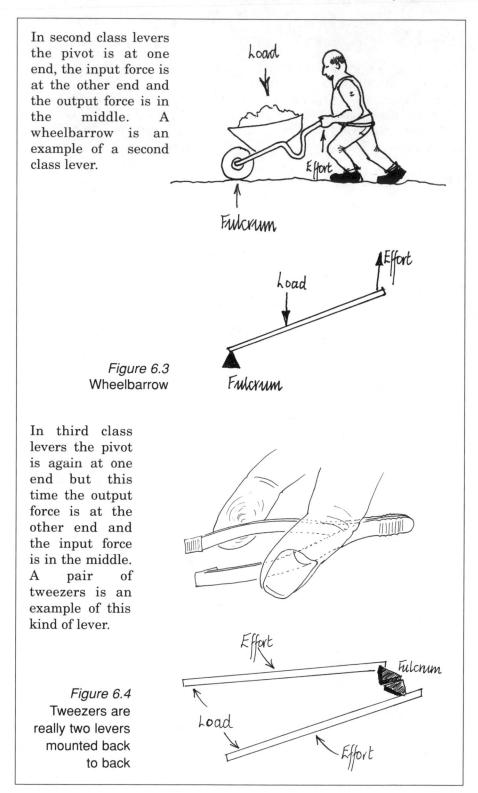

In second class levers the pivot is at one end, the input force is at the other end and the output force is in the middle. A wheelbarrow is an example of a second class lever.

Figure 6.3
Wheelbarrow

In third class levers the pivot is again at one end but this time the output force is at the other end and the input force is in the middle. A pair of tweezers is an example of this kind of lever.

Figure 6.4
Tweezers are really two levers mounted back to back

A selection of gadgets incorporating levers, such as a simple weighing scale, clothes peg or pedal bin, can be brought into the classroom for the children to examine closely and to assess how they work and how effective they are in terms of function and ease of use. The children's attention can be focused by asking them to sketch mechanisms and attempt to represent them diagrammatically. Eight year old Ginny, for example, worked out how a pedal bin worked and drew a diagram for others to follow (figure 6.5).

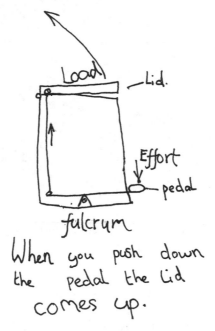

Figure 6.5   Ginny's diagram of the pedal bin mechanism

Outside the classroom we are surrounded by a wealth of devices involving levers and linkages, emphasising their importance and wide range of applications. Agricultural machinery, construction equipment, fairground rides, cranes and lifts often incorporate a range of simple and quite complex linkages.

Model making

A visit to an industrial museum provides a good source for highly visible linkage systems, e.g. the sack hoist in a windmill or the mechanical semaphore signalling systems at a railway museum.

After a trip to a preserved steam railway, some of the ten year old children in one school attempted to model the signalling mechanisms they had seen using a mixture of construction kits and consumable materials such as card and stripwood. The purpose of the constructional activity was not to make an accurate representation of the devices they had seen, but to try and mimic the motions they had observed.

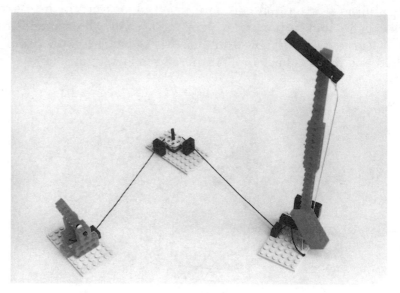

Figure 6.6   Lego signal mechanism

Figure 6.6 shows Hugh's and Tom's model of part of the signalling mechanism. They were fascinated by the way the lever in the signal box was able to make a signal move some way down the track. They tracked the motion from the lever, through the linkage system in the signal box, through the wire supported by small pulleys alongside the track, to the signal post and on up to the signal arm. Their model represented the signal lever and the signal arm with a simplified linkage system between the two.

Although the study of levers strictly falls in the province of science, it is sometimes useful to develop children's understanding of levers in the context of a technological activity.

As part of a topic on Romans, a class of eight year olds had become very interested in Roman weapons of warfare. One group decided to make a model ballista. They were, however, unaware of the significance of the position of the fulcrum in maximising the effort exerted on the load and were rather disappointed that their models did not project things very far. This gave the teacher the perfect opportunity to develop the group's, and later the whole class's, understanding of levers. After some experimentation with levers (rulers), movable fulcrums (pencils) and loads (erasers), the children applied their new-found knowledge to the design and construction of their own models.

Children selected one of three ways to provide the effort:

- winding up an elastic band, inserting the lever and using this as a sprung pivot
- using an elastic band to pull down the end of the lever
- putting a weight (blob of plasticine) on the end of the lever.

The most successful ballista proved to be one which incorporated all three energy sources (figure 6.7).

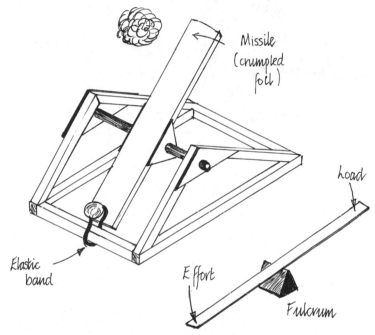

Figure 6.7 Model ballista

Shadow puppets

Levers can be encountered and studied in a range of contexts.

An infant teacher, seeing how fascinated her six year olds were by the visit to school of a puppeteer with shadow puppets, decided to use this as a context for introducing simple levers and linkages to her class. Since the limbs of human and animal bodies, like the operating rods of shadow puppets, are principally a series of levers and linkages, the teacher chose their bodies as a starting point. Following discussions about way their arms and legs moved, the children drew pictures of themselves showing where the joints were (figure 6.8).

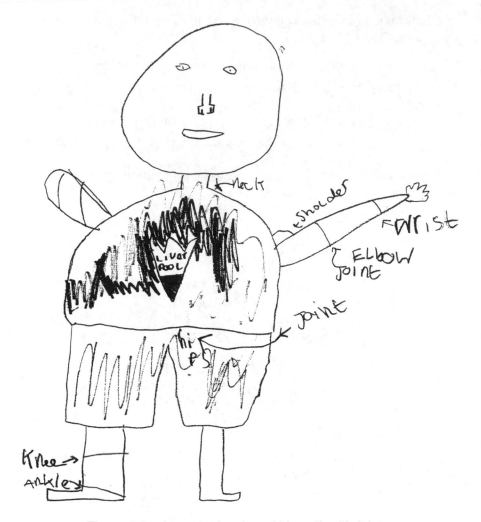

Figure 6.8 James's drawing of himself, with joints

The next stage was for the children to make an animated shadow puppet of themselves. Most of the children knew which parts of their drawings should move, but had no idea how to make this happen. Until they had developed some knowledge of simple linkage mechanisms they were unable to progress.

The teacher organised some practical tasks to help the children gain some understanding of fixed and flexible joints. At first they experimented with stiff card strips to explore the difference between glued joints and flexible joints made with paper fasteners. The next step was to make matchstick-like people from card strips, with limbs which bent in the right places. The children then explored the effect of putting control-rods in different places. They found that if a rod was attached to an arm between the shoulder and elbow, the puppet's forearm could not be controlled; but if the control rod was attached firmly (i.e. a fixed rather than a flexible joint) to the middle or end of the forearm, the whole arm could be controlled (e.g. figure 6.9). The children were were now able to make movable shadow puppets of themselves.

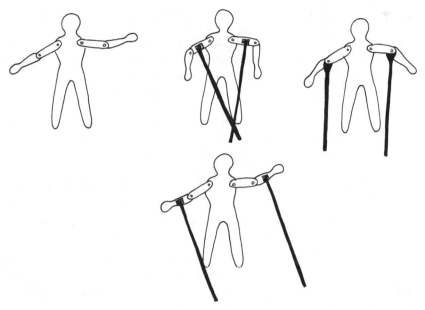

Figure 6.9   By placing control rods at different places on the arms, more control is possible.

Shadow puppets provide an excellent context for exploring linkages and levers. As the silhouette of the puppet is all that will be seen, the children can concentrate on perfecting the movements of the puppet without having to worry unduly about its appearance.

Animal puppets provide a range of opportunities for developing linkages. Ten and eleven year old children find simulating the different movements required to make the wings of a bird flap, the neck of a giraffe bend down, the legs of a frog leap or the fins of a fish swim, quite challenging! Animation does not have to be restricted to people and animals. Successful shadow puppet plays have been performed in which a fireman cranks up an extending ladder on the fire engine while another unreels a hose. One of the most imaginative productions witnessed involved a series of circus acts in which the lion tamer was eaten by a lion, the strong man lifted an impossible weight and the ringmaster was shot out of a cannon.

Puppetry in general provides a valuable context for building children's understanding of linkage systems. Shadow puppets are only one form. By making rod puppets, marionettes and life-sized muppet-like puppets, children can develop understanding of a range of mechanisms and simple control. This is explored in more detail in Chapter 10.

Pop-up books and cards

Children love pop-up books, and they provide a very creative approach to introducing mechanisms. The range of movements, and hence the complexity of the linkage systems, can be greater with pop-ups than with shadow puppets, and so form a natural progression.

Having enjoyed looking at a number of such books, a class of eight and nine year olds were set the challenge to write story books, with pop-up mechanisms, for younger children in the school.

After careful examination of some published books, the children were encouraged to speculate on how the mechanisms might work. The teacher had also prepared a set of example linkage cards, each demonstrating a different lever or linkage mechanism. (The mechanism however, was concealed inside the card which was kept closed by paper clips). The children were able to observe the input and output motion and were asked to predict the structure of the mechanism, before opening up the card to study its actual working (figures 6.10, 6.11).

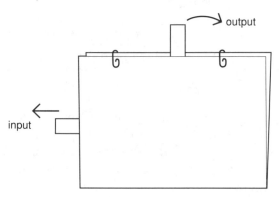

Figure 6.10   Closed linkage card

The children then went on to design their own animated scenes by applying or adapting these ideas.

Sarah and Michelle used a linkage similar to the third linkage in figure 6.11 to make the whale swallow Jonah when a lever was pulled as shown in the following diagram (figure 6.12).

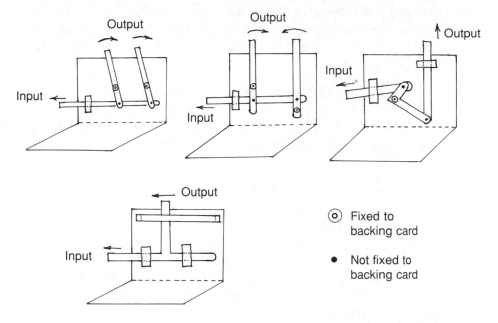

Figure 6.11 A set of linkage cards can provide a library of ideas

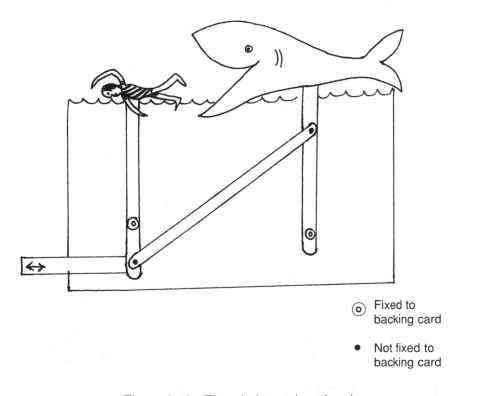

Figure 6.12 The whale catches Jonah

For the older children, reading and showing their books to the younger children was the culmination of the activity, but for the younger ones it was the beginning! All were now very eager to make their own 'moving books'.

This was quite a challenge for their teacher. She decided that a suitable response would be to involve the children in making simple moving models, made from card and simple fasteners, to animate excerpts or scenes from some of the their favourite stories.

Fortunately she had some experts on hand. The older children were charged with the responsibility of helping the younger ones develop an understanding of some of the simpler linkages. Using their favourite picture books as a starting point, the younger children selected a part of a story which they wanted to animate. Armed with strips of card and paper fasteners, linkage cards and the experience gained from making their own books, the older children experimented with the younger children until ideas for solving the movement problems were found.

The following diagrams (figures 6.13, 6.14) represent some of the card solutions produced by children in response to the movements suggested by the story.

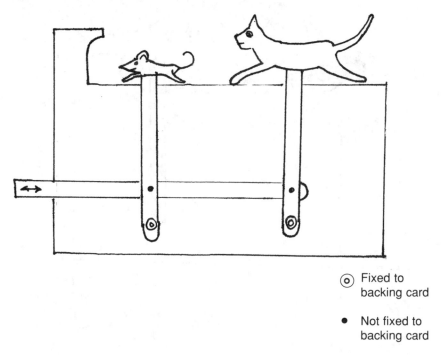

⊚ Fixed to backing card

● Not fixed to backing card

Figure 6.13 Can you help the mouse keep away from the cat? from *The Church Mice at Bay* by Graham Oakley

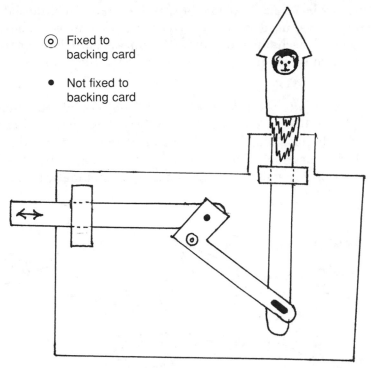

Figure 6.14 Can you help baby bear take off in his rocket from the chimney? from *Whatever Next* by Jill Murphy

Not only did the activity introduce the younger children to simple linkage systems, but it also helped the older children reinforce their understanding through their 'teaching'.

Up to now, the linkages we have studied have all been manually operated. The input motion (pulling or pushing a lever) is directly transmitted through the linkages to the output motion. When greater force needs to be transmitted, or the motion needs to be transmitted over a greater distance, or if the link between input and output needs to be flexible, a pneumatic or hydraulic system could prove more effective.

Pneumatics and hydraulics

Air, when placed under pressure, can be used to make things move. Commercial pneumatic systems are capable of exerting considerable force to lift or move heavy loads. The most obvious example of the use of pneumatics is perhaps the pneumatic drill, which uses compressed air as its power source. Other examples include pneumatic systems to operate doors or braking systems.

Hydraulic systems use fluid instead of air, and are used in situations where greater forces need to be exerted or transmitted. These include the arms of mechanical diggers, the rams used to crush cars in a scrap yard, the braking system of a motor vehicle and some modern lifts.

Children can investigate the power of air to lift objects by attaching a balloon or plastic bag to a plastic tube. When they blow into the tube, the bag or balloon inflates and can be made to lift a heavy object such as an encyclopaedia. A group of seven year olds tipped Humpty Dumpty off his wall by means of a simple pneumatic system (figure 6.15).

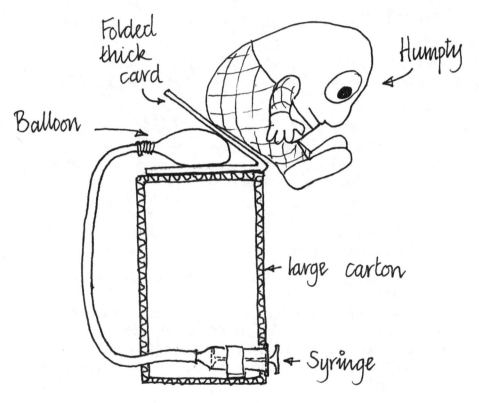

Figure 6.15   Humpty Dumpty is tipped off his wall

Although pneumatic systems are quick and easy to make, children soon appreciate their limitations. The shape of the balloon means that it can exert force in an unpredictable way and the inflation and deflation of the balloon is difficult to control.

Pneumatic and hydraulic systems for the classroom

Pneumatics systems make use of air pressure. Hydraulic systems make use of fluid pressure (usually oil in real life systems, but water in the classroom).

A pneumatic or simple hydraulic system can be made from two plastic syringes attached to each other by a piece of plastic tubing.

Figure 6.16   Pneumatic/hydraulic system made from syringes

When force is applied to one syringe (i.e. the plunger is pushed in), the pressure is raised throughout the whole system and the plunger in the other syringe is forced out and can be used to perform a useful action,e.g. open a door, raise an object. The syringe where the plunger is pushed in, is known as the master syringe and the one where the plunger is being pushed out, is called the slave syringe. If the plunger in the master syringe is pulled out again the plunger in the slave syringe will return to its original position.

Syringes usually have capacities of 5 ml, 10 ml and 20 ml. Since

force = pressure x area

the larger the syringe the greater the force it produces. Using a 20 ml master syringe and a 5 ml slave syringe will cause the 5ml plunger to pop out with some force and, although children will enjoy the effect, it could be a potential hazard in the classroom.

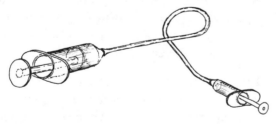

Figure 6.17
Pneumatic/
hydraulic system
where syringes
are of different
sizes

Although a hydraulic system can be made simply by filling the plastic tube with water, a smoother and stronger effect can be achieved by connecting both syringes to the plastic tubing and taking out both plungers before immersing the whole system in water. This expels the maximum amount of air. If one plunger is then pushed into one of the syringes while the system is still under water, and the other plunger carefully inserted in the second syringe, the resulting system works very effectively.

Ten year old Nicola made a beautiful Jack-in-the-box using pneumatics. Although delighted with the box, she was disappointed with its performance. When she pushed the operating syringe down, the air in the tubing made the operation of her Jack-in-the-box spongy and 'Jack', instead of springing dramatically out of his box, wheezed out flaccidly. By filling both syringes and the tubing with water, Jack's response was improved considerably. With the teacher's help, Nicola had turned her pneumatic system into a hydraulic system. Because water is harder to compress than air a hydraulic system gives a more immediate and firm response.

By linking syringes with tubes joined with a T-piece, a system can be created which has two outputs (figure 6.18).

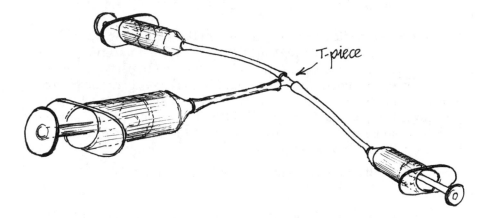

Figure 6.18   System with T-piece and two outputs

Rebecca and Mhairi adopted this technique when they wanted to make lifting barriers for a model railway system. By depressing a 20 ml syringe, the two 10 ml syringes were actuated simultaneously to raise the barriers on each side of the track.

Some construction kit manufacturers, most notably Lego, incorporate pneumatic systems in some of their kits. Apart from the obvious advantage of precision in construction, these commercial kits usually provide some sort of control system.

This Lego model of a dentist's chair (figure 6.19) incorporates two valves which can be used to control the height and angle of tilt of the chair in a way not dissimilar to the real thing. The control valves work by diverting the flow of compressed air to push the piston up or down the operating cylinder. By turning the valve one way air is

Figure 6.19 Lego model dentist's chair

forced in below the piston in the cylinder, forcing it upwards. When the valve is switched the other way, air is forced into the cylinder above the piston, pushing it down. It would be difficult to model this double-acting form of pneumatic cylinder without precision equipment (figure 6.20).

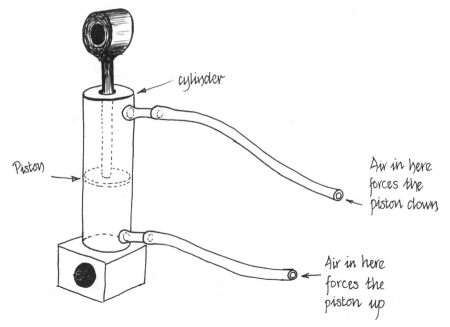

Figure 6.20 Lego double-acting pneumatic cylinder

Conclusion

Pneumatics and hydraulic systems can be made by children of all ages in the primary school although expectations and demands for complexity, precision and quality of finish would vary depending on the age and previous experiences of the children. This is equally true for systems incorporating levers and linkages. Puppetry and paper engineering have the added advantage of providing a highly visible and accessible means of introducing children to mechanisms in creative and imaginative contexts linking technology with such areas of the curriculum as language, drama and art.

Further Reading

The following books are full of ideas for constructional work with paper and puppet making.

Gowers P & Salisbury J (1990), *Paper Engineering,* Blackie

Johnson P (1992), *Pop-Up Paper Engineering,* Falmer

Tyler J & Gibson R (1990), *Paperplay: Lots of play ideas for Young Children,* Usborne

Chapman G & Robson P (1991), *Making Books,* Simon & Schuster Young Books

Bailey V & Robson D (1991), *Puppets,* Franklin Watts

Blanchard H (1991), *Puppets,* Wayland

Wright L (1990), *Puppets,* Franklin Watts

7 Making with mechanisms

Introduction

Cranks, gears, wheels;
Bearings, axles and hinges!
Cams, cogs, shafts;
Pulleys, levers and linkages!
Pinions and ratchets!
Couplings and sprockets!
Castors, clutches and windlasses!

Kelly (aged 11)

People seldom become poetic about, or enthused by, mechanisms. For many, there is an air of mystery or baffling complexity associated with things mechanical. There are some who attribute machines with some sort of intelligence or animism. "Stupid machine!" "Please, please work this time!" Against this background, the primary teacher is expected to develop children's understanding of mechanisms progressively and systematically, and in such a way that the children's interest, excitement and involvement are maintained. Most problems when working with mechanisms in the primary classroom, for children and some teachers, stem from the mismatch between aspirations and expertise.

Gary's automatic coin sorter, for example (figure 7.1), was a wonderful idea on paper, but was never constructed, owing to the complexity of its mechanism, the paucity of the school's resources, and, most significantly, the lack of experience of the constructor. The teacher also admitted to having insufficient knowledge or confidence to support Gary in turning the two-dimensional design into a three dimensional device.

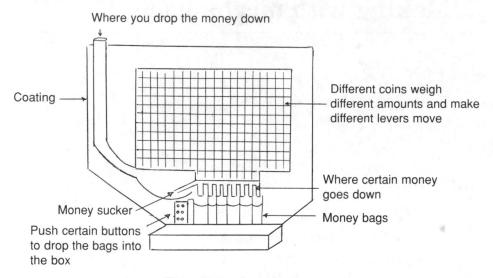

Where you drop the money down

Coating

Different coins weigh
different amounts and make
different levers move

Where certain money
goes down

Money sucker

Money bags

Push certain buttons
to drop the bags into
the box

Figure 7.1   Gary's coin sorter

This chapter attempts to provide ideas and suggestions as to how mechanisms can be introduced to children in such a way that they stimulate interest while systematically developing children's knowledge, skills and understanding.

At the same time, the place of construction kits is explored. How can they can be used to support children's learning, and how can they be managed in the classroom to ensure they are readily available, and yet remain intact?

Mechanisms – what are they?

So what exactly is a mechanism?

Mechanisms and types of motion

A mechanism can be thought of as a black box. Some sort of motion is put in and is transferred, translated or transmitted to an output motion which differs in some way from the input motion. The mechanism could change the speed, direction, power or type of motion.

Motion can be categorised as:

Linear – straight-line motion, such as a child travelling down a slide

Rotational – round and round motion, such as a wheel

Oscillatory – swinging motion, such as a pendulum

Reciprocatory – back and forth motion, such as a bicycle pump.

In the previous chapter we saw simple mechanisms like levers and linkages being used by children to control linear or reciprocatory motion. In this chapter we look at pulleys and gears, which are mostly associated with rotary motion.

Contexts and progression

There are essentially two different ways in which children's understanding of mechanisms, and their skills in constructing and using them, can be developed. The first is primarily teacher-led and the other involves a more open-ended problem-solving approach. Both approaches have their advantages and disadvantages and, as one might expect, a balance is to be recommended.

Teacher-led activity

Primary teachers have always appreciated the value of direct experience for children's learning, and it follows that many teachers choose examining and deconstructing everyday objects as a starting point.

Figure 7.2 A nine year old's exploded drawing of a can opener

The children who produced these exploded drawings of a can opener (figure 7.2) were developing their understanding of the structure and workings of the device. Such an approach encourages analytical scrutiny of an object, and provides children with the incentive to use graphical skills, and the insight to improve the quality and accuracy of drawings of their own designs. There are any number of everyday mechanical objects which can be used in this way e.g. hand whisk, corkscrew, hand drill, mangle, salad spinner, car jack and vice.

On a larger scale, a spinning wheel provides an excellent opportunity to examine the application of a range of mechanisms – particularly the crank and pulleys. By pushing the treadle up and down with a foot, the spinner turns the large flywheel. This is connected via a thin leather belt to the spinning head. As this turns, the fibres are twisted together to form thread and, at the same time, the thread is wound onto a bobbin.

Figure 7.3   Spinning wheel

Types of motion involved in a spinning wheel

The oscillatory motion of the operator's foot is transferred via the treadle to the vertical rod which reciprocates. The rod is attached via a crank to the wheel, and changes reciprocating motion to rotary. The belt on the wheel transfers the rotary motion to the spinning head. The speed at which the spinning head rotates can be altered, by placing the belt around one of two different sized pulleys attached to the head.

Georgina's diagram (figure 7.4) communicates her grasp of the mechanical principles of the wheel.

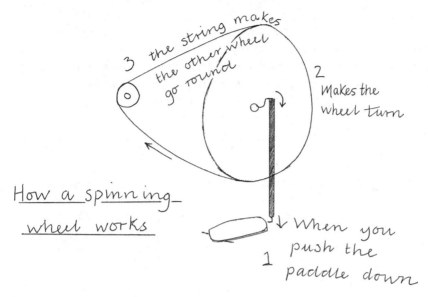

Figure 7.4   Georgina's spinning wheel diagram

The crank

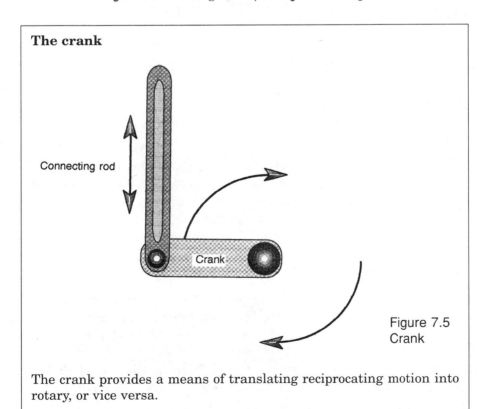

The crank provides a means of translating reciprocating motion into rotary, or vice versa.

While drawing can raise children's awareness of the workings of a mechanism, hands-on experience is more likely to develop their understanding.

During a residential trip to Snowdonia, a class of ten and eleven year old children visited a slate mining museum, and were impressed by the size and scale of the Victorian machinery. All the equipment in the mine was powered from one enormous water wheel, which had its motion transmitted around the workshops through a series of pulleys and shafts.

Pulleys and shafts

A pulley is a wheel with a groove around its circumference into which fits a belt. Rotational motion is transferred from one pulley to another via the belt. The speed and power of the motion can be changed by altering the size of the pulley. A small pulley linked to a large pulley will slow down the speed of rotation, but increase the power of the larger. A shaft is another name for an axle – the rod which passes through the centre of a wheel.

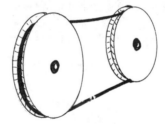

Figure 7.6   Simple pulley system

Back in the classroom, the teacher decided that making a model of the workshop's pulley system could provide the children with an excellent opportunity to experiment with pulleys of various sizes, as each piece of machinery connected to the shaft needed to operate at a different speed. It was a very ambitious project, but the teacher felt that if she worked alongside the children it could result in a very productive learning activity.

They succeeded in transferring the energy from a model water wheel, via a set of plastic gears, to the lay-shaft (so called because it lays horizontally) which ran the whole length of the model workshop. Three pulleys of various sizes, two of plastic and one of wood, were positioned on the shaft above each machine in the model. A belt transferred the motion from the pulleys on the lay-shaft to the pulleys on the machinery below (figure 7.7).

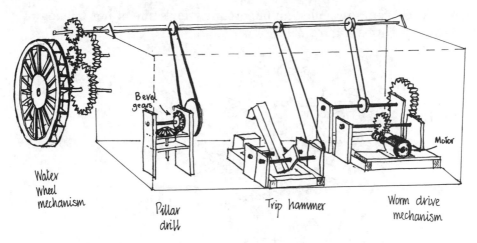

Figure 7.7 Diagram of water-powered workshop model

Pulley mechanisms are undoubtedly the best and most reliable form of transmission for children's mechanical devices made from everyday materials, wood or plastic, because unlike gears, they do not need precise alignment to work satisfactorily.

A bicycle provided a valuable class-based resource for an examination of mechanisms with a class of eight year olds. The brake system provided examples of the application of levers and linkages, while the pedals demonstrated the principle of the crank. Vicky's diagram and explanation shows how the crank converts oscillatory to rotational motion on a bicycle (figure 7.8).

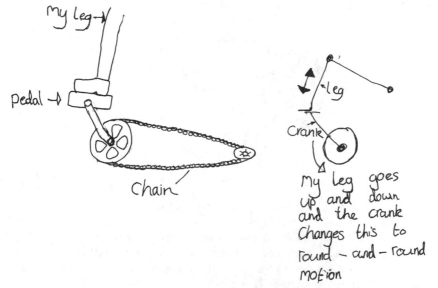

Figure 7.8 Vicky's drawing and explanation of a crank

The bicycle gears provided an opportunity for some of her friends to study gear ratios (figure 7.9).

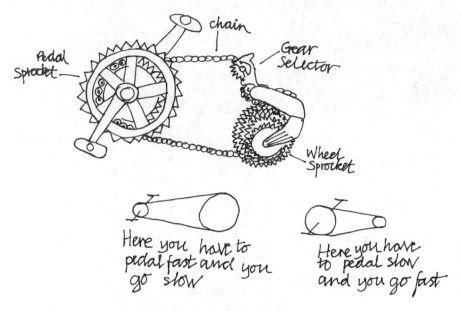

Here you have to pedal fast and you go slow

Here you have to pedal slow and you go fast

Figure 7.9 James's explanation of how his bicycle gears work

Gears and sprocket wheels

The gears on a bicycle are really sprocket wheels. These are linked by a chain just as pulley wheels are linked by a belt. A sprocket wheel and chain system is less likely to slip than a pulley and belt system.

Figure 7.10 Sprockets

Gears, on the other hand, transfer their motion by having their teeth in direct contact. Gears are sometimes incorrectly called cogs. The word cog is another name for a tooth on a gear. A gear can be called a cogged (or toothed) wheel.

So far the activities described have been representational. The children have seen examples of mechanisms and then drawn or constructed copies of them. One advantage of this approach is that the teacher can ensure that all the children have the opportunity to familiarise themselves with certain important mechanisms. In addition, the introduction of new ideas can be paced appropriately. It can also be a more comfortable approach for the teacher with less experience in this area. It is difficult, however, to be certain to what level the children have really understood the principles involved, as it is only when they are required to apply their knowledge in the solution of a problem that they really demonstrate their understanding of the principles of mechanical transmission.

A problem solving approach

A class of ten and eleven year olds was studying mountains and valleys; and groups had selected which modes of mountain transport they wanted to try to model. A rack-and-pinion railway, a ski lift, a cable car and a cliff railway were made and worked quite effectively. The four-wheel drive vehicles they made were, however, more aesthetically pleasing than functional. The teacher decided that the mechanical aspect of these models needed developing, and so set a challenge. Could the constructors make a motorised vehicle which could climb a slope steeper than one-in-one i.e. 45°?

The challenge caught the children's enthusiasm and several other children decided to try join in. Lego Technic was available in the school in sufficient quantities to allow five pairs to build models. Within a short period the teacher realised that although the children were familiar and appeared quite proficient with Lego, they were unable to apply their knowledge to designing and making a mechanism which would slow down the output from a motor to such an extent that it would increase the vehicle's power to haul its weight up a slope.

The children, however, clearly understood the importance of connecting a small gear to a large gear to reduce speed and increase power. Robert, a lively nine year old busily constructing a gearbox, explained his understanding of a 4:1 gear ratio as follows:

> When the little gear turns right round, only twelve teeth on the big gear will have gone past. So the little gear will have to turn right round again for another twelve teeth to go past, then again, and again ... So the little one will have to go round four times to make the big one go round once.

Simple gear train

A simple gear train comprises a series of directly interlinked gears.

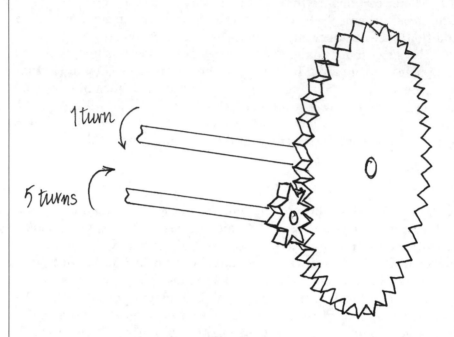

Figure 7.11   Simple gear train: 40:8 = 5:1

The motion is transferred directly from one axle to the next through the meshed gear teeth. The first gear in the train, the driver gear, has 8 teeth and the larger gear with which it has contact has 40 teeth. As, using Robert's explanation, the smaller gear will have to turn 5 times for all 40 of the larger gear's teeth to have passed by, the gear ratio of this system is **5:1** i.e. five turns leads to one turn. Another way of expressing this ratio is to use the numbers of teeth on each gear. The ratio is therefore **40:8**, which is the same as **5:1**.

Notice the opportunities for multiplication and division to be modelled practically with gears. The world's first computer, designed by Charles Babbage, capitalised on the mathematical relationships of gear ratios.

The children's difficulty stemmed from their inability to extend their application of this knowledge of the simple gear relationship to the construction of a compound gear train.

Compound gear train

A compound gear train has more than one gear on each axle (shaft) and the motion from the handle is repeatedly transmitted from small gear to large gear, from one axle to the next.

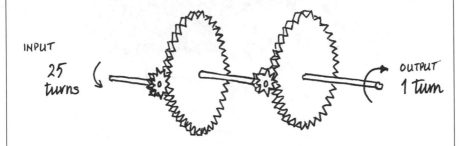

Figure 7.12 Compound gear train : 5:1 x 5:1 = 25:1

The gear ratio in this system is (5:1) x (5 : 1) = 25 : 1. This means the handle on the first axle will need to turn 25 times for the final gear to revolve once. The best way for the children to find this out is to experiment with different sized gears and count the number of turns required each time. This is one way in which construction kits can assist the learning process, as exchanging gears is relatively simple.

At this point the teacher decided she needed to intervene, and demonstrate to the children the way in which two gears could be placed on the same shaft to construct a compound gear train. Her description of the children's responses confirmed for her the appropriateness in the timing of her instruction.

It was like a ray of sunshine breaking through the clouds. Until I showed them what to do they were just sitting there, sticking gears on axles in a sort of haphazard way. Once they got the hang of doubling the gears on the axles, they were fired with enthusiasm. They were off!

Before long, all five groups had built a vehicle which could grate and grind its way up the 1:1 slope. Although the children realised the problem was now how to make the wheels grip the slope, they were fascinated by the way in which the speed of rotation was being drastically reduced with the addition of each new axle to their gear train. They asked if the challenge could be changed to discover who could construct the slowest vehicle – the tortoise challenge!

Figure 7.13   The tortoise challenge: a slow vehicle

The slowest vehicle, pictured here, travelled a distance of 4 millimetres in one minute (24 cm per hour).

"If we had more Lego, we could make it take a year to go a millimetre!" was Robert's and Tony's concluding evaluative comment.

This example shows one major advantage of this approach, namely that of capturing, maintaining and building on the children's interest and enthusiasm. It was their problem – a crucial ingredient. Another advantage is that the children are learning on a 'need to know' basis, and therefore have a greater chance of retaining this understanding. It does, however, put greater pressure on the teacher, not only in terms of ensuring coverage and progression of different aspects of mechanisms, but also with respect to the breadth and depth of knowledge which the teacher needs to ensure that she can respond to the children's needs and take them further as required.

Worm gear

A worm gear is a very efficient way of transforming the speed of rotational motion in a mechanically simple way. One turn of the worm results in the worm-wheel to which it is connected advancing by only one tooth. Since there are 40 teeth on the worm wheel, 40 turns of the worm are required to turn the wheel once.

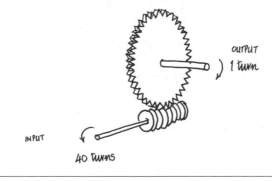

Figure 7.14
Worm gearbox:
40:1

Construction kits – how can they be used?

Most construction kits contain cards or sheets to guide the children's construction of various models, but successful construction of a model following instructions does not necessarily mean a child understands the principles of the mechanism involved. To demonstrate a thorough appreciation of gearing, children need to design and build their own mechanical devices. But children cannot be expected to create models with geared mechanisms without having had some prior experience. How can they gain this experience in an interesting and motivating way?

The following approach shows how construction kits can steer a way between the two approaches described earlier, teacher-led activity and a problem solving approach. Here ideas cards provide the basic understanding and skills techniques but the children are encouraged to develop this further according to their interests.

As part of their topic on fairgrounds, a class of older primary children created their own models of fairground rides from Lego. Building a mechanism to slow down the electric motor's speed proved to be the greatest problem for most of them. Their models provide an insight into the range of design solutions which can be adopted. As can be seen, the children's approaches demonstrate an increasingly sophisticated understanding of the principles of geared mechanisms.

Figure 7.15　Lego roundabout with worm gear

The boys who constructed this roundabout (figure 7.15) made a direct copy of that on the Lego construction card, but made some modifications to its appearance to 'personalise' their model. The mechanism was based around a motor and a worm gear, giving a 40:1 speed reduction. Although the boys did not yet have sufficient understanding of geared mechanisms to design their own gearbox, the teacher used their model to help them appreciate how the motion was being translated.

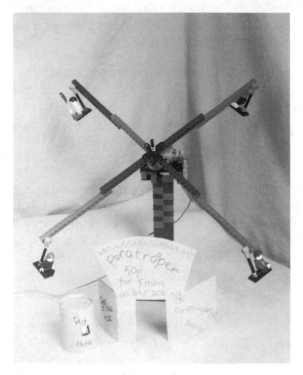

Figure 7.16   Lego 'paratrooper'

The children who constructed this model of a 'paratrooper' ride (figure 7.16) initially had problems making a mechanism which slowed the motor down to a realistic speed for their model. Their teacher suggested they looked at the gearbox mechanism for a vehicle described on one of the Lego cards. The group realised they need only follow the instructions for making the chassis and gearbox, and could then put the arms of their roundabout ride on the axle instead of the wheels. The Lego card helped them through the tricky stage of harnessing and controlling the motor, to realise their design.

It is worth noting that when it comes to pulley mechanisms, construction kits can be used to experiment with and make prototype pulley systems. In fact the precision needed to ensure the gears remain properly aligned is better achieved by using construction kits. However, it is possible to construct geared mechanisms from scratch using relatively inexpensive materials. Getting the required level of accuracy can be tricky, but a definite advantage is that these models can be taken home or become part of the classroom archives.

The organisation of kits

When children become engaged in activities which require the application of a range of mechanisms, this can create problems of organisation. Children who are experimenting with ideas can be constrained by the contents of their particular box of kit parts. If they raid another box, how can the teacher be sure all the components are returned? Sometimes, it can take longer to sort the bits and pieces out at the end of an activity than it did to make the model in the first place!

Teachers adopt different strategies to overcome this organisational problem including abandoning the manufacturer's boxes and sorting several kits into trays of similar parts e.g. a tray of wheels, a tray of gears, etc. Creativity is greatly enhanced, management is eased (provided the trays are located centrally) but stock-taking is harder. Security-conscious teachers tend to keep the more attractive/ expensive items e.g. motors and control boxes, under close scrutiny.

Conclusion

Although there are no hard and fast rules about the way and order in which children come to learn about mechanisms, the levels of complexity involved, both in terms of underlying concepts and in the skills required to build particular mechanisms, suggest a line of development.

Clearly, levers and linkages (see Chapter 6) are less conceptually demanding and require fewer constructional skills and less knowledge than pulley and gear systems. In most cases, levers and linkages are associated with manually operated systems, and so avoid the complication of the electrical circuitry needed for motorised mechanisms.

Examples of applications and activities which are appropriate for earlier stages include poddalump-type traps (see Chapter 6), pop-up books and cards, signalling systems (semaphore stations, railway signalling), early aeroplane flaps and controls, door locks, security devices and castle defences (e.g. drawbridge mechanisms, ballista and catapults).

At this point, simple systems for changing the type of motion can be introduced, for example the crank which changes reciprocatory motion to rotary or vice versa and can be found on bicycle pedals.

The ease with which pulleys can be incorporated into a model, and the readily available sources of real-life examples described earlier, provide a useful route from manually powered devices into motorised transmission systems. The ways in which the speed and direction of rotary motion can be changed can be modelled quite easily with pulley systems and, provided the contexts and activities are appropriate, children can come to appreciate the purpose and principles of transmission systems with relative ease.

Examples of appropriate contexts might include: Victorian industry, early farming (e.g. traction engine and powered threshing machinery), fairground rides, washing machines, vacuum cleaners, conveyor belts and escalators.

Working with geared mechanisms always appears to be more daunting, but need not necessarily be so. Provided the children have some understanding of pulley systems, and have experienced gears on a bicycle, the principles of geared mechanisms tends to be quite straightforward for them. In addition, one major advantage of gears over pulleys is their ability to transfer motion without slippage.

As a child Seymour Papert, one of the creators of the educational computer programming language Logo, found gear systems to be a valuable source of visual imagery to enhance his mathematical thinking (see Papert (1980), pp vi-viii). By representing mathematical problems as images of gears and manipulating their ratios, then 'counting' the numbers of rotations, he found he was able to solve quite complex mathematical problems. There is always a possibility that there might be young learners who could be inspired mathematically by being engaged in the construction of geared models.

Reference

Papert, S, (1980), *Mindstorms: Children, Computers, and Powerful Ideas*, Harvester Press

Further reading

The following titles are useful to develop understanding of mechanisms.

Catlin, D (1994), *The Inventa Book of Mechanisms,* Valiant Technology Publications

Macaulay, D (1988), *The Way Things Work,* Dorling Kindersley

The CD ROM, based on the above book, provides an interesting, interactive means of furthering understanding of mechanical devices:

Macaulay, D (1995), *The Way Things Work CD Rom,* Dorling Kindersley

8 Making with electrics

Introduction

Providing opportunities for children to experiment with batteries and bulbs has long been considered an appropriate activity for the primary classroom. What is different about electrical activities associated with Design and Technology? The principle difference lies in the objective. Since the goal of scientific investigation is the furtherance of knowledge, the purpose in experimenting with batteries and bulbs is to find out about electricity, how batteries work, the function of a bulb, or the properties of conductors and insulators. The driving force behind technological activity, however, is the solution of a problem. The batteries and bulbs are used to achieve an end result, e.g. lighting a model house.

This chapter aims to show, through examples of relevant technological activities, how children can develop their understanding of the application of electrical circuitry to the solution of problems of increasing sophistication and complexity. From simple circuits with batteries and bulbs to computer controlled devices, the underlying operating principles are the same. Although some understanding of the way in which a device functions is useful, for technological activity it is far more important to know how to use the device effectively.

Getting started: simple circuits

Fumi and Misha were determined to make a lighthouse after hearing the story of the *Lighthouse Keeper's Lunch*. Their teacher showed them how to make a circuit with a battery, a bulb in a bulb-holder and some wires, and the two girls set about making the tower from cardboard tubes and offcuts of card and wood.

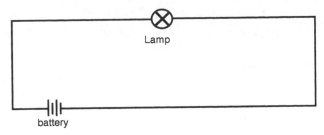

Figure 8.1 A simple circuit (battery and bulb)

They had little difficulty in installing the circuit but, when it was finished, they were obviously unhappy: "It doesn't flash! Lighthouses should flash!"

The teacher was faced with a dilemma. How far should she take them? She could:

1 Take out the existing bulb and replace it with a flashing bulb. This would solve the children's problem, but would not develop their understanding of electrical circuitry.

2 Replace the bulb with a flashing LED (Light Emitting Diode). This would at least extend the children's knowledge of a different sort of light source.

3 Show them how to make a simple switch from paper clips and drawing pins. This would introduce the concept of switching in a circuit, but would have to be operated manually.

4 Show them how to put a push-button switch into the circuit. This would introduce switches to them, but would they really understand how a switch worked?

5 Put an automatic flashing device into the circuit – perhaps a little too advanced for the children?

6 Use a computer to control the flashing of the lamp – perhaps a little over-ambitious at this stage in the children's learning, and was it really the most appropriate tool for the job?

She decided to show the two girls how to make a simple switch using paper clips and drawing pins. The girls were delighted, and even took their model to the headteacher, who suggested they display it in the entrance hall of the school for visitors to see.

A few days later the home-made switch fell apart, resulting from over-use by passing children. The teacher and the girls replaced it with a push-button switch mounted in a plastic sandwich box, which also housed the batteries.

As a starting point, these children needed some prior knowledge of circuits to help them design the original lighthouse, but the specification changed once the model was completed. The teacher was then able to choose the appropriate level of intervention, based on her knowledge of the children, her personal expertise and her knowledge of the resources available.

Progression: from bulbs to computers

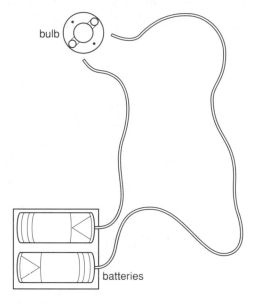

Figure 8.2   Open-ended circuit

A battery and two wires form the basis for a simple circuit. Between the ends of the open wires various low voltage components can be inserted to make a circuit, allowing the current from the battery to flow from one battery terminal through the component and back to the other terminal (figure 8.2).

Components

Components which can be placed in the circuit include:

- Bulbs or LEDs (Light Emitting Diodes) which can be incorporated into vehicles, display boards, house models, signalling devices, warning indicators and alarms.

LEDs

LEDs are used extensively in electronic equipment. An LED probably provides the red indicator light when you turn on the hi-fi. The advantage of LEDs is that they seldom fail, unlike a bulb which has a limited operational life. Their disadvantage is the small amount of light they emit and the difficulty of connecting them. A piece of connector strip is a quick and easy way of providing a connector for an LED. The two bare wires of the LED are inserted into one side of the connector strip and the screws tightened. Wires leading to a battery can then be inserted into the other side of the connector strip and the screws tightened to form a secure circuit. It should be noted that LEDs are polarity-dependent. If an LED does not seem to work, swap the wires round to allow the electricity to flow the opposite way through the LED.

- Buzzers and bells, which can provide sounds for vehicles, doorbells, alarm systems and warning devices such as on a model of a level crossing. Fumi and Misha, for example, could have added a fog horn to their lighthouse model.
- Motors. These are a little more difficult to incorporate as they usually require some sort of mechanism to harness the motor's output. However, if the required rotary motion needs to be fast, and does not need to be particularly powerful, e.g. a fan, a rotating bow tie for a clown, helicopter rotor blades, then no mechanism will be necessary.

Switches: the beginnings of control

Once the children have some appreciation of simple circuits, their next requirement is likely to be some sort of control. In most cases this will take the form of a switch.

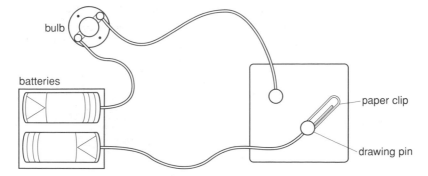

Figure 8.3   Circuit with home made switch

Switches

A switch is simply a means of breaking one of the wires in a circuit to interrupt the flow of electricity. A switch can be placed anywhere in a circuit.

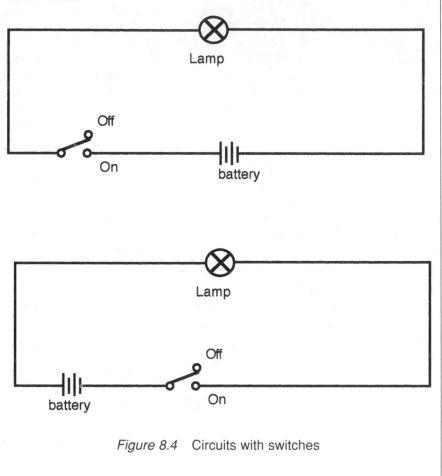

Figure 8.4   Circuits with switches

Children often assume that, as a switch has two contacts, it should be connected directly to the battery in the same way as other devices. Although this will have the effect of controlling the light, the switch, when turned on, is making a short circuit.

Short circuits

The electricity is by-passing the bulb and flowing directly from one terminal of the battery to the the other. With normal dry cells, this will have little effect other than warming up the battery and running down its voltage in a short space of time – i.e. ruining the battery. If this were done with rechargeable batteries – even accidentally - then more disastrous results could ensue. The wires could act like electric fire elements and glow red – causing quite serious burns if a child happened to be holding them. Worse still, cheap rechargeable batteries have been known to explode! For these reasons:

Rechargeable batteries should never be used by children for electrical experiments or to power their models!

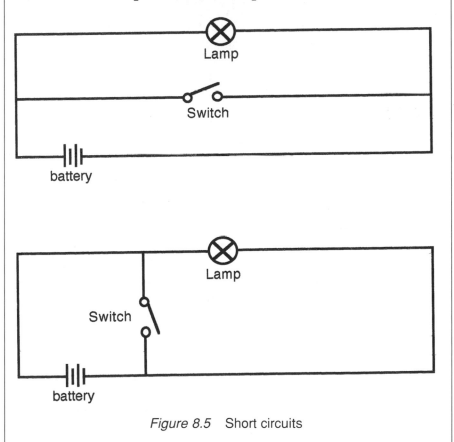

Figure 8.5   Short circuits

Switches come in a remarkable variety of forms.

Types of switches suitable for primary school use

Name of switch	Appearance	Real life applications	Classroom uses
Toggle switch		Light switches, switches in cars, lever-type switches on hi-fi and electronic equipment, etc.	Most types of circuit where a device or component needs to be left on or off for long periods e.g. a light, a motor
Push switch or push-button		Doorbell button, keys on a calculator or computer keyboard, the horn button in a car	Any model or device where a component needs to be on only while a button is being pressed e.g. a morse-code signaller, a buzzer acting as an alarm or doorbell. Can also be used as a sensor to detect if a vehicle has bumped into something
Push switch (push to break)	This switch looks exactly the same as a push-button, but it switches off when it is pressed	The switch which turns on the light when the fridge door, or a car door opens. Sensor switches in cars and some household burglar alarms	Any device or model where pressure is required to turn something off e.g. a sensor on a vehicle to turn off the motor if it hits a wall.

continued ...

Name of switch	Appearance	Real life applications	Classroom uses
Push-push switch This switch stays on (latches) when pressed and needs to be pressed again to be turned off		Often used in table lamps	As they are often very small and very cheap, and require only a small hole for mounting, these switches are a very good replacement for applications where toggle switches could be used
Slide switch		Sometimes used in radios or hi-fi often where there is limited space	For the same sort of applications as the toggle switch. It has the advantage that it is often smaller and requires less effort to operate – making it easier to mount
Micro switch		These are often unseen switches They are like push switches, but can be made very small to fit inside tight locations, such as in the button on a computer mouse or inside a telephone, to sense when the receiver has been removed	Any device or model where only a small amount of pressure is required to turn something on or off e.g. to sense when a crane's jib is fully elevated

continued ...

Name of switch	Appearance	Real life applications	Classroom Uses
Rotary switch (Unlike a volume control on a radio or TV, this switch clicks as it turns - each 'click' can turn on a different device)		Used to be found on televisions to change channels. Now found on expensive hi-fi equipment and on some automatic washing machines	Limited applications, but because of their ability to switch on a range of different devices, can be used to control model traffic lights or stage lighting in a model theatre
Reed switch (Turns on when a magnet is passed across it)		Principally used as door and window sensors in household burglar alarms. The magnet is held in the window frame, while the reed switch is mounted in the window frame to detect when a window opens	Model burglar alarms, or any device or model where movement or position needs to be sensed without physical contact e.g. to discover when a model train has passed by, to sense when a robot arm is in a particular position
Reversing switch or **Double pole double throw** (DPDT) or **Double pole change-over (DPCO) switch**	Note how the wires are connected to the switch to achieve reversal of the current	Although the switch illustrated is a slider switch, a reversing switch can come in a variety of forms. It is used mostly to reverse motors or mechanisms e.g. to open and close an automatic door, to wind up or wind down the electric windows in a car	Any application where a motor needs to be reversed e.g. a model vehicle, the motor winding or unwinding the string for a model crane

Most electrical devices include some sort of switch, operated either manually or automatically. A washing machine, for example, includes switches to control the level of water in the tub, to monitor the temperature of the water, to sense whether the door is open or closed, to control the rotation of the drum and to enable the operator to turn the machine on or off.

Home-made switches

When Joanne, Mina and Simon were making their model petrol station, they decided to add a warning bell to alert the garage owner when a car arrived. They constructed a pressure switch from wire and aluminium foil. When a car drove over the switch, the bell sounded (figure 8.14).

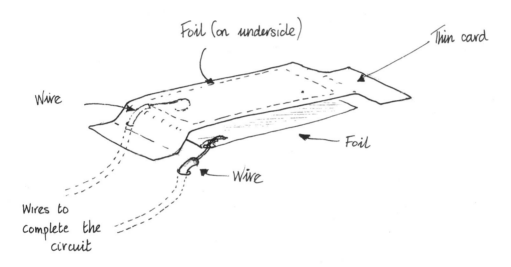

Figure 8.14   Home-made pressure switch

The girls who made a museum room took great delight in booby-trapping the doors and the exhibit, to detect and deter intruders. Home-made switches were placed under the carpet, over the door, and beneath the statue. The one under the statue worked in the opposite way to the other two in that it detected when the statue was removed, rather than when pressure was placed on it. Any one switch closing would cause the alarm to sound. Incidentally, the girls were investigating the foundations of logic circuitry.

Logic circuits

Basic logic gates are used to detect three states – AND, OR or NOT.

In this circuit, the lamp will light only if switch 1 *and* switch 2 are operated.

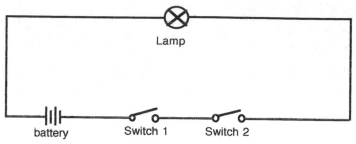

Figure 8.15   AND circuit

In this circuit, the lamp will light if either switch 1 *or* switch 2 is operated.

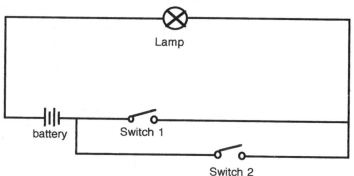

Figure 8.16   OR circuit

In this circuit, the lamp is on until the switch is operated. In other words, the lamp is on if the switch is *not* operated.

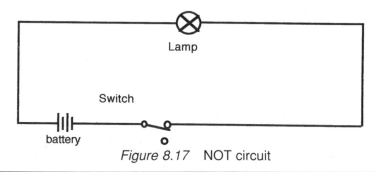

Figure 8.17   NOT circuit

The museum alarm circuit (figure 8.18) is an example of OR logic gates. The alarm will sound if the switch over the door, *or* the switch under the carpet, *or* the switch beneath the statue is operated.

The switch under the statue will operate when the statue is *not* there.

The girls placed a master switch on their battery box so that the alarm could be turned on and off. For the alarm to sound, one of the sensors (under the carpet, over the door, under the statue) needed to be operated *and* the master switch needed to be on.

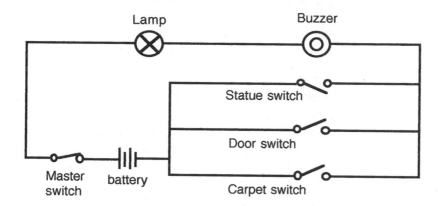

Figure 8.18   Diagram of the museum alarm circuit

Switches with motors

Electrically there is very little difference between wiring a motor into a circuit and any other component. It is likely, however, that some sort of control over the motor will be required. The least complicated form of control will be a simple on-off switch. As was described in the previous section, it does not matter whereabouts in the circuit the switch is positioned, provided it can cut off the flow of electricity from the battery to the motor.

What is often more useful is some sort of control which will reverse the current to the motor; for example, this would enable a model vehicle to reverse. The simplest way of reversing the motor is to swap over the wires, either on the battery or on the motor. Although this will achieve the desired objective it is not a very elegant solution. A reversing switch (see p 126) is a more technically appropriate way of solving the problem. The switch is wired up so that the positive and negative leads from the battery will be connected one way round if the switch is in one position, and the opposite way round if the switch is clicked to the other position.

Control and computer control

A control box in its simplest form consists of a box in which are mounted a few switches and, possibly, an energy supply in the form of batteries. It is possible to make or buy small control boxes with various switched outputs, including a reversing switch. These have the advantage that one control box can be used on several separate occasions connected to different models.

Control boxes with several outputs can be used to control several models at the same time.

Once the children have grasped the idea of a control box as little more than a box with a battery and a few switches, the next logical step is to investigate computer control. Lego Dacta's Control Centre provides a useful half-way house. The Control Centre can be used as a straightforward switchbox and power supply. In direct mode, by pressing the buttons controlling the three outputs, children can operate their models from one central location. The advantage the Control Centre has over a home-made control box lies in its ability to remember the sequence and duration of key presses, in a similar way to that in which a programmable robot or turtle will carry out a program of instructions.

Bhupinder and Josey were delighted with the model lift they had made by following the instructions on one of the Lego cards (figure 8.19). In only a few seconds, they had attached leads to the Control Centre and were pretending to be lift operators.

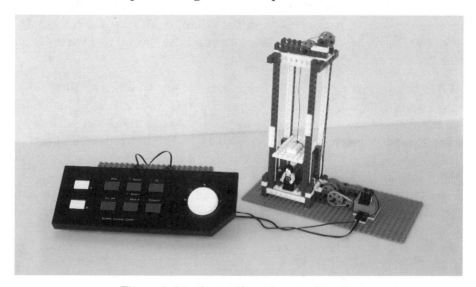

Figure 8.19   Lego lift and control centre

When they had played for a while, the teacher showed them how to program the Control Centre. This was achieved simply by holding down one of the two memory buttons for a second or two. The girls then entered the the series of instructions needed to operate the lift and pressed the STOP button. Now, by pressing the GO button, the Control Centre repeated their actions at any time, and as many times as they required. They had programmed the Control Centre to operate their model.

The Control Centre has the big advantage of operating independently from a computer, but it has its limitations. When operating the Lego lift it was unable to detect when the lift was at the top or bottom of the lift shaft. It simply implemented the instructions irrespective of the starting point. The first instruction entered by the two girls raised the lift from the ground to the first floor. This was fine when the lift was on the ground. Unfortunately, when Bhupinder and Josey tried to implement their program a second time, their first program had left the lift at the top. The lift tried to go up further and the whole structure collapsed under the strain. The girls needed to write another program which would make the lift go down.

If the Control Centre had known the lift was already at the top of the shaft (by means of a sensor), it could have been programmed to ignore the 'up' instruction, and operate a 'down' instruction instead. To achieve this, the next stage would be to remove the Control Centre and insert an interface which, when connected to a computer, would put the model under computer control involving the use of sensors.

Computer control and feedback

The nine year old children in one junior school class had visited a supermarket as part of a study of their local environment. Michael and Jonathan decided to build a model of the conveyor belt on one of the checkouts. They were fascinated by the way the belt automatically knew when to stop when something was on it, and carried on rolling when it was empty.

The conveyor was relatively easy to make and was controlled initially with a simple switchbox. However, this was not automatic. The teacher showed the children how the motor could be controlled by replacing the switchbox with an interface connected to a computer. Now they could operate the conveyor by typing instructions into the computer (figure 8.20). Finally, by adding a light sensor to the end of the conveyor, they learned how the computer could be programmed to stop the motor, and hence the conveyor, when something stopped light from reaching the sensor, i.e. when something passed by on the belt. When they next visited the supermarket, the boys were delighted to discover the conveyor belt at the checkout worked in exactly the same way.

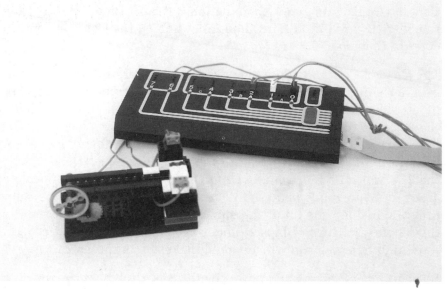

Figure 8.20   Lego conveyor with interface

Most computer control interfaces have a series of input channels as well as outputs. Up to eight different sensing devices – to measure light intensity, sound level, temperature, angular position, electrical resistance or touch – can be connected. The computer can be programmed, for example, to monitor conditions in a greenhouse (model or real). A window could be programmed to open and close depending upon the temperature. A fan could be programmed to turn on if things became really hot, or a heater when things cooled down too much. A computer, through an interface, could even be programmed to monitor the moisture levels in the soil (by measuring its electrical resistance), and turn on a sprinkler system if the soil were too dry. Nowadays most commercial horticulturalists have computer control systems monitoring their greenhouses. Through the use of a simple interface, children can begin to appreciate the way in which the computer can be used to replace a switch box and a human operator.

Like the Dacta Control Centre, a programmable turtle is 'blind', and if wrongly programmed will not know if it has bumped into a wall or is trying to push a chair out of the way. The Roamer programmable turtle, however, has the facility for adding sensors. If a touch sensor is added to the front of the turtle, it can be programmed to go backwards as soon as it touches an obstacle (figure 8.21).

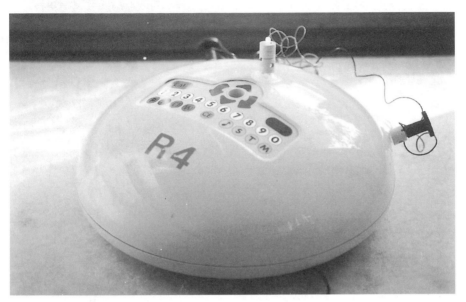

Figure 8.21   Programmable Roamer robot with touch sensors and LED

Claire and Megan, two ten year olds, were interested in finding out how long it would take a Roamer to escape from a simple maze constructed from house bricks – a square enclosure with a gap in the middle of one wall. They discovered that by changing the angle by which the Roamer turned after bumping into a wall, sometimes the Roamer would never escape, sometimes it would escape almost immediately, and with some angles it would only escape after a large number of collisions. They discovered that 'awkward' angles such as 13°, 27° and 59° were better than neat angles such as 45°and 20°).

> *"With neat angles, the Roamer keeps going round the same way, but with awkward angles it will keep going round different ways until it finds the way out."*   Claire

For the girls, the programming of the Roamer became a means to an end rather than an end in itself.

The big-wheel model which Emma and Sarah made for the class's fairground model was a prime candidate for computer control (figure 8.22).

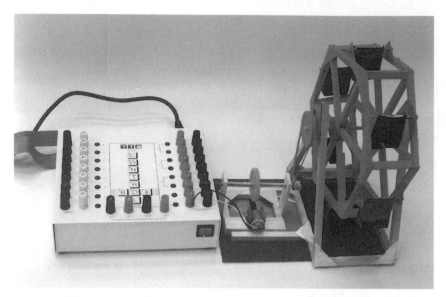

Figure 8.22   Big wheel model connected to interface

To operate realistically, the wheel had to rotate for a set period, then stop to release its passengers. At first, the girls did this manually but, when they saw some of the other children operating their models with the computer, they wanted to use the computer to control theirs. The batteries and switch were discarded and the wires from the motor were plugged into the interface. The program to operate the model was very simple. It consisted of three instructions: one to turn the motor on, the next to wait for thirty seconds, and the third turn the motor off.

They were very happy with this until one of the boys in the class pointed out that the passengers in one of the seats would never be able to get off as it was always at the top of the wheel when it stopped!

The next stage in programming was a little more complex. The girls added a few more instructions which stopped the motor six times at precisely timed intervals, to release the passengers from each carriage.

The next level of complexity would have been to add to their model a sensor, which could detect precisely when each carriage was at the bottom of the wheel, and stop the motor then. The teacher decided, however, that this extra level of complexity was not appropriate at this time but noted that this was an area which should be introduced to Emma and Sarah in the not too distant future.

Conclusion

There is a natural line of progression with electrical circuitry. Starting from simple circuits with batteries and bulbs, we move onto the use of alternative devices such as buzzers and motors before moving into control through simple home-made switches and then on into applications requiring different sorts of switching operations e.g. a burglar alarm. Next, the children can make and/or use simple switchboxes to control their models. Finally, they can move on to computer control systems – a rational step from the switchbox.

The extent to which Design and Technology work on the application of electrics is integrated with a scientific study of electricity, is a choice the teacher has to make. The extent to which the knowledge and understanding of electricity can be fostered through Design and Technology as opposed to direct teaching is largely dependent upon the quality of the activities which are organised and the level of teacher intervention. Although a discussion of these issues is beyond the scope of this chapter, it is something which a teacher needs to consider when planning work in this area.

Further reading

The following publication is particularly useful for explanations of scientific concepts, including electricity:

Wenham, M (1995), *Understanding Primary Science: Ideas, Concepts and Explanations*, PCP

The following books focus on electronics:

Beasant, Pam (1990), *Introduction to Electronics*, Usborne

Duncan, Tom (1977), *Adventures with Electronics*, John Murray

Mims, F.M. (1983), *Getting Started in Electronics*, Radio Shack (available from Tandy or Radio Shack stores)

Penfold, R.A. (1977), *Beginners' Guide to Building Electronic Projects*, Bernard Babani Publishing

There are very few books which provide specific information about control technology but the following provide some useful background information:

ASE/DATA (1994), *Understanding Control*, ASE

Kellett, J & Jinks, D (1993), *Design and Make – Folio 10: Computer Control*, DJK Technology

9 Product evaluation

Product evaluation is something which constantly engages us. When buying new garden furniture we look at the range on offer, considering its robustness to stand up to the rough and tumble of a young family and dog, how well the materials with which it is made will stand up to being left outside in all weathers, how comfortable it is, the ease with which an elderly person will be able to get into and up from the chair, the quality of the finish, whether or not the design appeals to you and fits in with the style of the garden, how easily it can be moved around the garden, and environmental considerations relating to the materials used. The 'best buy' for us depends upon the furniture which meets the priorities which we personally place upon the criteria identified as important to us.

But product evaluation can also involve more detailed investigation. Which brand of oven chips or frozen hamburgers to buy involves trying several brands and getting feedback from the family on preferred taste, texture and, of course, value for money.

And there is another level at which product evaluation can be pursued. This involves disassembly, perhaps just to satisfy one's natural curiosity, but more likely as a way of looking at other people's solution to a problem to get ideas for solving similar problems of our own or developing a new idea. Industry calls this *reverse engineering*. Disassembly need not involve an irreversible taking apart of a product. Temporary or semi-permanent fixings can always be removed, but much can be done by careful examination and deduction about what is happening in the unseen areas.

Developing children's ability to engage in product evaluation needs to address all these aspects; and is closely linked with developing their curiosity, their questioning and investigation skills, their ability to observe closely, imagine, take things apart carefully and make judgements based on relevant criteria.

Sometimes it is easier to develop this aspect of design and technology in the classroom with focussed tasks where the teacher identifies particular aspects of product evaluation on which she wishes the children to concentrate. This chapter mainly describes this type of activity, although there are also examples of teachers integrating product evaluation within 'design and make' projects.

Product detectives in the infant classroom

Since technological development is frequently the perfection or redesign of a manufacturing process rather than the invention of a completely new product, it is important that children have the opportunity to investigate processes by which products have been made as well as the quality, form and efficiency of the finished products.

Visits to production lines help to evaluate and understand processes, but much can be deduced about the way a product has been made by careful examination of the end product itself. All finished articles contain clues about the design and manufacturing process, and children can be encouraged to assume the role of detectives and find the clues to the stages and order of production. A close look at finished products will also question the initial purpose, and ask how well the choices made during the process of design address that purpose.

In the activity described below the class teacher is starting two young children along this path.

Listen to two seven year old detectives exploring the application of colour and method of construction of two 'play people'. One, a model of Gaston, from Disney's *Beauty and the Beast*, is made from a single moulding and the detail painted on later. The Lego person has been assembled from different coloured plastic pieces.

LOUISE   *(pointing to Gaston)* This one's made of rubber.

EMMA   Yeah...rubbery plastic.

LOUISE   *(pointing to the Lego person)* That one's made of plastic. They got all the different colours they needed, shaped them and stuck them together ...

EMMA   And painted them!

LOUISE   No. It's coloured plastic. They didn't have to paint him. They just had to put the bits together.

EMMA   *(examining the Lego person)* And they made him twist; his head twists.

LOUISE   That's 'cause he's made in bits. It's made out of 1, 2, 3, 4, 5, 6, 7, 8 – 8 bits. There's a line on that one – there's two bits. *(She then picked up Gaston)* Yeah! They made him how they wanted him – the bumps and the smooth bits – and painted them.

EMMA   *(running her finger down a seam on Gaston)* It's … it's, you know, like you made … like that moulded teddy you made.'

The two girls, drawing on their previous experiences, demonstrated a degree of understanding of the different processes involved. The teacher asked how they could test whether their idea that Gaston was made of painted plastic was correct. Closer examination of the sole of his shoe revealed where some of the paint had been chipped off to show a spot of creamy plastic below. The girls were convinced.

A closer look at the Lego person resulted in a complete disassembly – with some help from the teacher and several large tools. The children were then asked to try to re-assemble the figure and record the order in which they assembled the pieces by drawing a story board (figure 9.1).

Physically taking products to pieces is not always necessary when the components can be seen to be separate and the fastening process imagined. Visualising the undoing can, however, be tricky for young children and using products which children can manage to dismantle, like textiles or pop-up books, is helpful in developing this skill.

Recognising that a product is assembled from separate components leads to consideration of the assembly processes. The teacher developed this by asking the children to bring in a collection of toys. They then discussed together how a toy aeroplane or truck might have been assembled, and the children were asked to consider where choices could be made in the sequence of construction. Where toys were easy to take apart and re-assemble this was done, and the children drew story boards showing the sequence for re-assembly. Encouraging children to question the sequence of construction helps them to focus on the need for planning. Taking apart products, laying out the components and considering when holes were drilled or pieces painted helps to support the chess-like thinking that is hard to consider while engaged in original designs. Recognising that some operations become impossible, as access is blocked by permanently fixing components too soon, can be a hard lesson to learn when engaged on the task: 'I should've put his cloak on before I stuck his head!'

Figure 9.1 Two records of the process of assembly of a Lego person.
The sequence on the left was drawn after looking closely at the figure.
The sequence on the right was recorded after the figure had been
disassembled and the children had worked out how to assemble it

In this classroom, the teacher's principal aim in involving the children in a product evaluation activity was to develop their ability to plan and sequence their own construction activities.

Analysing the appropriateness of materials

In another infant classroom the teacher had brought together a collection of drinking cups. She wanted her five and six year olds to look at these products from other people's points of view, and also to focus their attention on the appropriateness of the materials for the intended user.

The collection showed different designs and choices in response to the same basic need. They ranged from babies' drinking cups and children's decorated beakers to china cups and wine glasses. All were displayed on an 'interest table' and several strategies were employed to encourage the children to consider the materials and the users of the cups.

In one game a child chose one characteristic of the cups, for example being 'see-through', and sorted the collection into two groups, without giving her reason to the rest of the group, who then had to try to work out the criterion for sorting. Through this activity the teacher aimed to highlight similarities and differences in the materials used to make the cups.

Another activity involved placing question cards alongside the cups to help the children think about the collection

Who might need a cup with a straw?	Which cups are for hot drinks?	Which cup would be best for you?	Which cup would your Mum choose?

In addition to the question cards a collection of pictures of different people, male and female, young and old, were left on the table. Children were asked to choose cups for the different people and talk about making things to suit different people.

Two six year old girls were examining and discussing the collection ...

KIM   These have got straws in and this has got a cover.

LIZZIE   This is a nice design and the fish inside makes me think I'm drinking sea-water or something – and I can see Ariel.

KIM   And it's got a straw that you fold away.

LIZZIE   I think the ones with straws are easier to drink from. All you've got to do is pull this up.

TEACHER   Which do you think would be best for you?

KIM   This one would be best for me and my friends *(indicating the Little Mermaid flask)*.

LIZZIE   That one would be good for my little brother. *(indicating the Aladdin flask)*

KIM   And the cover cup for a baby.

TEACHER   What about this for a baby? *(indicating the bicycle bottle)*

KIM   That's a cycle thing and it's got no handles.

LIZZIE   Yeah and it doesn't close properly.

KIM   And it might leak all over the place.

LIZZIE   Those aren't safe. *(indicating tea cups and glasses)*

TEACHER   Why not?

LIZZIE   Cause if you drop them they break.

KIM   *(Indicating the wine glass)* That one isn't 'cause if you bite the glass you would cut your mouth ...

TEACHER   Why do you think somebody chose to make it out of glass then?

KIM   Cause it looks pretty.

LIZZIE   They're nice but they're just made out of a bad thing.

KIM   They might be my Mummy's favourite, 'cause Mummy likes drinking wine.

This exchange indicates quite a high level of reasoning behind the choices and comments that the two children are making. They are demonstrating understanding of the properties of materials beyond their practical experience. By thinking about the users of the products the children are considering the appropriateness of materials for different purposes. It takes time to draw young children on from evaluation that only considers their own perspective. The children here are considering the views of someone younger than themselves which allows them to apply a previously held perspective. It is an important step towards understanding the idea of fitness for purpose and moving away from a unique meaning of 'best' i.e. best for them.

Alison, aged four, on her introductory visit to school, was attracted to the interest table and keen to talk about the collection of cups. She selected the cup with a picture of Princess Jasmin from *Aladdin* as her favourite.

TEACHER   Why did you chose that one?

ALISON   Because I love Jasmin, 'cause I like her dress, and I love the tiger and Jasmin.

As you would expect she viewed the containers very subjectively. However, when asked which one would be the easiest to drink out of she readily conceded that other designs could be better for other users, having first established that she was not going to be asked to use them!

ALISON   *(indicating the Jasmin beaker)* For a four years, drinking in that.
          (indicating the training cup with lid) For a baby in that and they won't spill it.
          (indicating the bicycle water bottle) They could have that too, 'cause it has got a lid.

Similar activities can be set up to develop children's awareness of other construction issues such as fastenings, but their appreciation and understanding of the wider issues associated with product evaluation the views of the user, or appropriateness of design) can only be built up by constantly revisiting the issues in a variety of contexts.

Product detectives in the junior classroom

The investigation table is a common feature of infant classrooms but often considered insufficiently challenging for older children. However, by structuring sorting activities and careful selection, product evaluation and investigation activities can be tailored to extend understanding at all levels. The following example shows how another curriculum area can provide a meaningful context for this type of Design and Technology activity.

Analysing fastenings

As part of a history topic, a collection of World War II artefacts was augmented by the loan of clothes and household items from the grandparents of a class of eight and nine year olds. There were uniforms, a splendid collection of hats from tin helmets to berets and bush hats, and of course a gas mask. There was also a good collection of everyday items: an old radio, a flat iron which had to be warmed against the fire, wartime recipes, ration books, large wrap-round aprons, hair curlers, children's shoes and clothes, including a liberty bodice and long woollen handknitted stockings, and a large doll dressed in baby clothes from the 1940s complete with towelling nappy and large safety pin.

Clearly the display acted principally as a focal point for the classwork in history. But once the class were familiar with the collection, the teacher decided that she could also use it as a stimulus to revisit and reinforce issues related to product evaluation.

In one activity, aimed to focus the children's attention on different fixing and fastening techniques, the class teacher mentally selected one of the items from the collection and the children tried to identify which it was by asking direct questions about the way it was joined.

> *Is it joined with tape?*
>
> *Can it come apart?*
>
> *Is it meant to come apart?*
>
> *Does it have a kind of fastening that we use today?*
>
> *Could a child fasten it easily?*

The game was played with a small group of children and the teacher only answered 'yes' or 'no' as the children tried to guess which item had been chosen. In another group game a child made a silent selection of a type of fastening and then made statements such as "I like the coat but I don't like the gas mask." All these statements were governed by the fact that all the things 'I like' must have the fastening that was selected and all the things that 'I don't like' must not be joined in that way. Children were invited to show that they had guessed the chosen fastening by joining in with statements of their own which followed the rule.

The selection of products was very skilful in this instance, providing a range of temporary and permanent fastenings. Arguments which questioned the inclusion or exclusion of a product inevitably arose, but led to further refinement of statements.

John had chosen fastenings which could be undone:

ALEX   You said you liked that beret. It doesn't come undone!

JOHN   The stitching round the edge could!

Jane had chosen stitching:

DEBBIE   You should have said you liked that book. It's got stitching inside, see!

The liberty bodice with its small buttons and suspender fastenings intrigued some of the children. Today's tights were seen to be a great improvement!

'Best buy': evaluating nappies

The teacher had initially included the nappy on the doll to draw the children's attention to the safety head on the pin. However, it was the idea of using an old towel as a nappy that caught the attention of some of the children, most of whom had small brothers or sisters. They were initially very dismissive about the 'old-fashioned' nappy. The teacher, wanting to challenge the children's assumption that new ideas are necessarily better than old ones, asked one group to consider the advantages and disadvantages of towelling and disposable nappies. She suggested that they start by considering what a nappy needed to do. "To stop things round the baby from getting messed up," was the prompt reply; but as further comments didn't take the matter much further the teacher showed the children examples of best buy reports where star ratings are given to different hi-fi systems or types of washing machines. She drew their attention to the range of criteria on which different products were judged, and asked the children to come up with an equivalent set of criteria to help them decide which was 'best' between a disposable or towelling nappy. She also suggested they ask grandparents and parents for their opinions.

A few days later the group came back and this time they had plenty to say! The suggested criteria included:

- softness
- keeping the baby dry
- cost
- saving time
- how easy the nappy is to put on
- environmentally friendly

Initially they dismissed some decisions as easy – disposable nappies saved time, but the first thought that towelling nappies were cheaper "because you only buy them once" was challenged when one of the children pointed out the costs involved in washing and another child declared emphatically that you still needed to buy plastic pants to put on top. The criterion which produced most discussion was the last. The children were quite concerned about pollution. What happened to disposable nappies? One of the children, an advocate for disposable nappies, was however quick to point out that washing machines used a lot of electricity and electricity was energy and we shouldn't waste energy.

Clearly many of these issues could have been investigated more rigorously, but on this occasion the teacher decided to leave matters there. Her purpose had been achieved. The children were now much more aware of the range of issues to be considered when making judgements and evaluating products.

Understanding design: musical instruments

In the following example a class of eleven year olds was engaged in a music-related design-and-make activity. The class teacher had brought together a fascinating collection of musical instruments from several countries. The wind section included an African clay whistle, a bamboo pipe with bamboo reeds, an old hardwood fife and an original tin whistle. The strings comprised a Bedouin stringed instrument, a mandolin, a ukulele and a guitar. There was also a finger piano from Zimbabwe and a variety of pitched and non-pitched percussion instruments from the music corner including xylophone, glockenspiel, claves and castinets. The teacher wanted to focus on similarities between design solutions across cultures and use the collection to develop technological understanding.

Although the children were keen to start making their own musical instruments straight away, the teacher felt that it would be beneficial for them to investigate materials which vibrate and resonate before embarking on their own designs. One activity involved the children in making simple reeds. Drinking straws were flattened and cut to a point at one end. Careful blowing down the straw, with the sharpened end right inside the mouth, caused the straw to vibrate. The children were encouraged to record the way that the pitch changed as the straw was cut shorter. Reeds were then placed inside the ends of different pipes and the different tones and qualities of the sounds discussed. Another activity involved placing a musical box mechanism on sheets of different materials to observe the effect.

When it came to making the instruments, one group designed a stringed instrument which relied on a large coffee tin to amplify the sound rather like a tin banjo (figure 9.2).

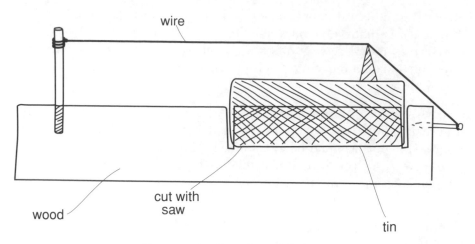

wire

wood

cut with
saw

tin

Figure 9.2   Drawing of tin banjo

Late in the project they were experiencing difficulty maintaining the tension on their string, as their design of tuning peg kept slipping. This meant that that they could not maintain sufficient tension in the string for it to vibrate.The teacher directed them to the instrument collection where they grouped together the different solutions for string tensioning. The Bedouin stringed instrument and the ukulele both had tuning pegs while the mandolin and the guitar had different types of machine heads involving worm gears (figure 9.3).

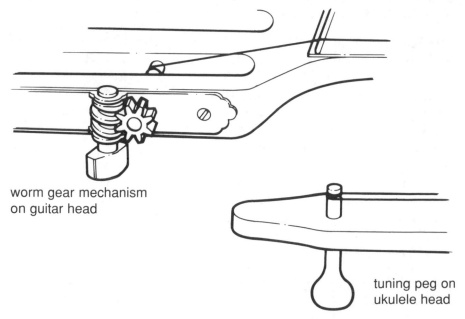

worm gear mechanism
on guitar head

tuning peg on
ukulele head

Figure 9.3   Tuning pegs on ukulele and worm gear mechanism on guitar

The pegs on the ukulele and the Bedouin instruments were about as effective as their own design but the machine head on the guitar did not slip. The children and their teacher felt that the latter was worth investigating.

This group of children had looked at some simple mechanisms during a visit to a textile mill and had seen a worm gear being used to alter the supply of water to the water wheel.

Water wheel mechanism

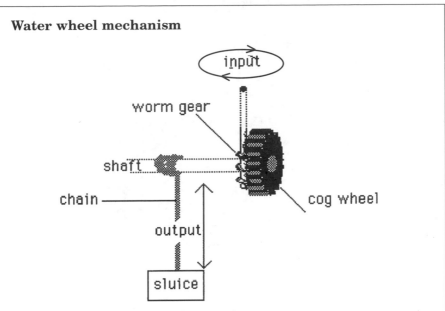

Figure 9.4   Water wheel mechanism

As the input shaft is turned, the worm gear, which meshes with the cogs on the cog wheel, rotates the cog wheel and its shaft to wind up or let down a chain connected to the sluice controlling the flow of water.

When the worm is rotated in one direction, it pulls the teeth of the cog wheel up and turns the shaft clockwise. When the worm is turned in the other direction the shaft turns anti-clockwise. While the worm can turn the cog wheel, the cog wheel cannot turn the worm. Since it is a one-way system, despite the weight of the sluice gate pulling on the cog wheel, the worm holds it (and the sluice gates) in place.

Wishing to deepen the children's understanding of gears to modify motion and force, the teacher brought out a large poster showing the mill mechanism. She reminded the children of the way in which the worm gear in the mill was providing a one-way system and compared this to the worm gear on the mandolin and guitar. Just as the worm gear mechanism in the mill allowed fine adjustment but remained firmly in place under pressure, the tuning system on the guitar needed to be able to turn in either direction to tune the string but not be turned by the pull of the string when the person tuning it let go.

With a little help the machine head on the guitar was disassembled and a model of a machine head made using a Technic construction kit which included worm gears (figure 9.5).

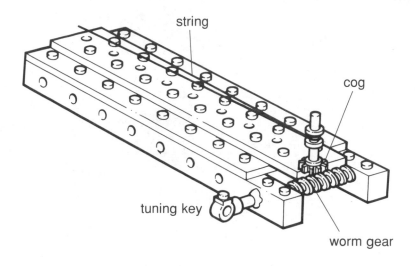

string

cog

tuning key

worm gear

Figure 9.5   Machine head with worm gear

Discussing the model with the children convinced the teacher that they understood what was happening:

MICHAEL   When you turn the handle and it turns the worm it winds the elastic band up dead slow.

TEACHER   What happens if you try to turn the cog wheel?

MICHAEL   You can't.

TEACHER   Why not?

MICHAEL   Because the worm won't let it.

A version of the worm gear, which could remain permanently on their model to keep the tin banjo in tune, was constructed out of plastic gears and the banjo was ready for playing!

In this classroom the children got ideas for improving the design of the tuned musical instrument which they were making by disassembling existing instruments and examining other people's solutions to the same problem and a similar problem in a different context, in this case a textile mill. When the instruments were displayed and discussed by the whole class, the teacher capitalised on this feature and encouraged the children to think more widely about the constantly evolving nature of technology. She was able to talk about the way in which technology from one area of application can be transferred to another one and how adapting existing solutions from previous experiences to new situations is an integral feature of technological progress (see Chapter 2).

Product evaluation and design: overalls

In this last example product evaluation again occurred as an integral part of a design activity. A group of nine and ten year olds were telling the dinner ladies about their ideas for their next Technology project which was to be based on textiles. Some were thinking of designing and making large cushion covers for the infant library, others soft toys for the nursery unit. One of the dinner ladies half jokingly remarked, "I wish you would design a new overall for us. We could do with a change."

The children were keen to take up the challenge and persuaded their teacher to let them have go. The teacher warned them that it might not be possible to implement their design and a compromise was reached regarding the end product of the activity. The children would simply present sample designs and recommended materials to the dinner ladies, who would select what they considered to be the most appropriate and give feedback to the children on their ideas.

The teacher arranged for the dinner ladies to be interviewed by the group. As a result of the interview, the children collected the following criteria for the new overall.

The material needed to:
• be spongeable
• not stain easily
• be quick drying
• be comfortable to wear i.e. not be too stiff and unyielding and not make people feel hot and sticky.
• not crease too readily.

As far as the style was concerned the dinner ladies simply asked that the overall protect their fronts and backs from sticky fingers and spillages. A large pocket was also essential.

The children set to designing the new overall. Three styles emerged. One was a slightly waisted, button-through dress with short sleeves, collarless V-neck and a large patch pocket. Another resembled an old-fashioned cook's apron with large bib and voluminous skirt, side pockets and large cross-over straps which tied at the back. The third was a simple tabard, with a large pouch across the front. It slipped over the head and fastened at the sides with velcro straps.

Samples of a range of materials of different colours and patterns were obtained and the children set about evaluating them against the identified criteria. Two children set up washing tests, which involved smearing test samples with a range of food products under control conditions i.e. regular-sized blobs. The washing test was followed by a drip dry evaluation. Another group devised a stiffness test which involved sliding a sample of cloth out over the side of a cupboard until it draped under its own weight to touch the side of the cupboard. The distances which each sample of material, all of the same dimensions, had to be pushed out before touching occurred were then compared. The stiffer the fabric, the further out it had to be pushed. A number of ideas were tried for the 'sweat test'. They included wrapping a damp sponge in fabric, wearing an arm band of fabric for a day and testing the water absorbency of various fabrics – none provided any conclusive results.

The dinner ladies were then invited to look at the designs and the suggested material – a cotton blend in an apricot colour with a small brown motif. They questioned the children's reasons for rejecting some of the other materials and approved of the material selected from the point of view of comfort, and because it did not show marks too readily. When it came to style they favoured the 'cook's apron'. A major factor in reaching this decision was the absence of outside pockets which tend to catch on table corners, chair backs and door handles.

Product evaluation was built into this activity at different points. Various fabrics were investigated for specific properties and the end product evaluated by the intended user. Feedback from this provided valuable experience for the children on the idea of 'fitness for purpose', the compromises involved and the importance of the priorities of the user when making final decisions. The chosen fabric did not come out best on all the criteria and the selected design was a compromise between what was practicable, comfortable and attractive; but both were the closest match to the needs of the user.

Conclusion

The examples in this chapter look at the use of product evaluation for developing understanding of planning and sequencing, properties of materials, fastenings and applications of mechanisms. But, while product evaluation can make sense in isolation, its value is enhanced when questions are asked about the consumer or user and issues related to values, quality and the notion of 'best' are considered. Most of the examples in this chapter, therefore, adopt this wider perspective, and the activities described aim to develop children's ability to evaluate according to a range of criteria and encourage them to enter into the debate between form and function from viewpoints other than their own.

Further Reading

Few books are dedicated specifically to product evaluation but, to assist in the theoretical disassembly of products, the following might prove useful:

Macaulay, D (1988), *The Way Things Work*, Dorling Kindersley

The way in which products have developed is covered in some detail in these books:

Baren, M (1992), *How it All Began: Stories Behind Those Famous Names*, Smith Settle

Tibballs, G (1994), *The Guinness Book of Innovations*, Guinness Publishing

10 Curriculum planning in the classroom

The ways in which class teachers carry out their individual planning, although often differing in detail, have nevertheless key features in common. A certain amount of time is allocated for activities which aim to achieve specified learning objectives. The model of planning which will be used in this chapter assumes that the school curriculum for Design and Technology is organised into a series of units of work. Each unit is designed to occupy a known block of time, and forms part of a series of such units to progressively develop children's skills, knowledge and understanding of Technology.

At the start of the school year a teacher will need to plan how the time allocated to Design and Technology is to be organised. It might be for example that a teacher of younger children will split the time into a series of small units, whereas the teacher of an older age group may plan two distinct units of study. Although a specific block of time in the year will be earmarked for Design and Technology, it is likely that a unit may overlap, or be integrated with other areas of the curriculum and so share in that subject's time allocation.

It is not intended that this chapter will consider how a unit of study will specifically be organised – whether the hours are delivered as, say, a series of weekly sessions or a blocked week of study – but rather how the different types of activity which form the unit could be structured – for example, how a unit of a specific number of hours might be organised to ensure that new practical skills and understanding are acquired by the children through a series of focused practical tasks, integrated design-and-make activities, and the evaluation and disassembly of products. In addition, opportunities for assessment and ways forward will be indicated.

In this chapter we shall examine the organisation of three example study units carried out with three different age groups. The first, 'Puppets', was planned as a self-contained Technology unit for a vertically grouped class of five and six year olds; and was designed to develop the children's knowledge and understanding of the properties of different materials, to introduce the children to particular joining and fixing techniques, and to develop their making skills. Inevitably there were strong links with English, and at times, through the choice of puppet characters, some personal and social development. This unit in total took 15 hours of teaching time over a four week period. The second study unit, 'Textiles', involved eight and nine year olds in a wider ranging study lasting 20 hours, which linked with the mathematics, history and art curricula. The final 24 hour unit of study was conducted with a class of ten and eleven year olds and focused on developing understanding of mechanisms. It was linked with some science work on food types under the project title of 'Bread'.

Each case study shows how the class teacher attempted to develop the technological skills and understanding of the children through a series of planned activities.

Puppets

This study unit was carried out with a vertically grouped class of five and six year olds. There were also a few four year olds in their first term at school. The teacher was joined by a classroom assistant for the equivalent of three days each week and made use of a rota of parent helpers. The teacher knew the five and six year olds well, having taught them the previous year; but she knew very little about the four year olds' experience before they came into the school.

The five and six year olds already had experience of designing and making with a variety of materials e.g.

reclaimed materials: model buildings and vehicles
paper and card: masks
textiles: woolly chicks and finger puppets
plastic: cup and ball toys
construction kits: Bauplay, Lego Duplo.

All the children were reasonably proficient at cutting, folding and gluing. The six year olds had additional experience with wood and had made models incorporating simple mechanisms e.g. pop-up cards, one-string puppets, windmills on sticks and wheeled vehicles made from construction kits.

The teacher's principal aim for the next Design and Technology unit was to further develop the children's knowledge of materials and construction techniques and their skill in incorporating movement into their models. She also wanted to use this topic as an opportunity to assess the four year olds' practical skills and capabilities.

Design and Technology objectives for the unit

> *Designing skills*
>
> to develop the children's ability to communicate their ideas through talking and drawing
>
> to develop the children's skills in choosing materials based on their characteristics in relation to design specifications.

> *Making skills*
>
> **Four year olds**
>
> to develop the children's skills in
>
> • working with a range of materials e.g. paper, card, fabric and reclaimed materials
> • carefully marking out before cutting
> • cutting paper, card and fabric accurately with scissors
> • joining different materials with adhesives and tape
> • making flexible joints in card.
>
> **Younger five year olds**
>
> to consolidate and extend the above including the use of wood.
>
> **Older five year olds and six year olds**
>
> to consolidate the above and to develop the children's skills in:
>
> • cutting and shaping stripwood
> • making fixed and flexible joins with a range of materials and components e.g. card, stripwood, wire, string, fasteners

Materials and components

Four year olds

to develop the children's knowledge and understanding of:

- the working characteristics of different types of card, paper, fabric and adhesives
- flexible joints

Younger five year olds

to consolidate and extend the above

Older five year olds and six year olds

to consolidate the above and to develop the children's knowledge and understanding of the properties and working characteristics of stripwood

Mechanisms

Four, five and six year olds

to develop the children's abilities to incorporate movement into their models through the use of flexible joints

Control

Five and six year olds

to introduce the concept of control using rods and string

Context

A professional puppeteer had already been booked to visit the school during the term. The teacher decided that this could provide a valuable stimulus and an ideal context for the realisation of the Design and Technology learning objectives for the term. Before the visit, the children were asked to bring in a range of reclaimed materials (cartons, egg boxes, plastic bottles, plastic packaging, etc.). The teacher also visited a nearby fabric warehouse and bought several large bags of reject fabrics. Parent helpers were invited to school for the day of the puppeteer's visit.

After careful consideration the teacher selected the following activities to form the overall unit. The puppeteer was briefed on these overall plans.

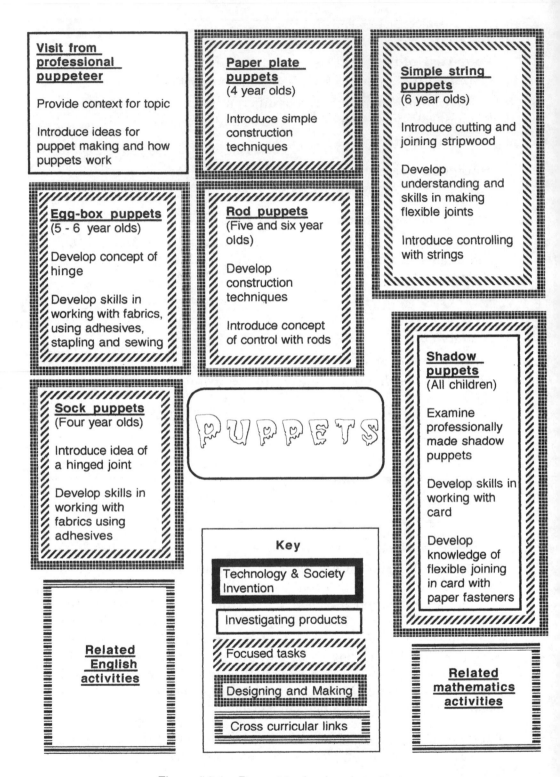

Visit from professional puppeteer

Provide context for topic

Introduce ideas for puppet making and how puppets work

Paper plate puppets
(4 year olds)

Introduce simple construction techniques

Simple string puppets
(6 year olds)

Introduce cutting and joining stripwood

Develop understanding and skills in making flexible joints

Introduce controlling with strings

Egg-box puppets
(5 - 6 year olds)

Develop concept of hinge

Develop skills in working with fabrics, using adhesives, stapling and sewing

Rod puppets
(Five and six year olds)

Develop construction techniques

Introduce concept of control with rods

Sock puppets
(Four year olds)

Introduce idea of a hinged joint

Develop skills in working with fabrics using adhesives

PUPPETS

Shadow puppets
(All children)

Examine professionally made shadow puppets

Develop skills in working with card

Develop knowledge of flexible joining in card with paper fasteners

Key

Technology & Society Invention

Investigating products

Focused tasks

Designing and Making

Cross curricular links

Related English activities

Related mathematics activities

Figure 10.1   Puppet topic planning chart

Description of unit activity

The puppeteer's visit

The puppet performance involved hand, rod and shadow puppets and had the desired effect of firing the children's enthusiasm. When the performance was over, the children were invited by the puppeteer to examine the puppets, to investigate the different types of materials used, how these had been joined together and how the puppets worked.

The children were encouraged to question why different materials had been chosen for different parts of each puppet e.g. latex (a kind of flexible plastic) for faces and hands, different textured and coloured fabrics for the costumes, and wood, plastic and wire for the support structure of the puppet. The children were particularly interested in the unexpected materials which had been used to make some of the puppets – hair made from wire wool, bodies made from modified cooking oil bottles, eyes consisting of marbles and the jewels made of crumpled sweet wrappers.

Puppet-making workshop 1: rod and string puppets

The next day, working in groups with an adult helper, the children began to design and make their own rod puppets.

Four year olds

The teacher took the opportunity to work with the youngest children on a carefully structured task: making a simple paper plate puppet. The children first designed their puppet's face on paper. They were encouraged to focus on the features and mood of the puppet – was it happy, frightened or sad? A paper plate formed the basis for the face of the puppet and the children made the features by choosing the materials which they considered would convey the mood which they had chosen for their puppet. They glued on oddments such as pieces of wool and parts of reclaimed materials (egg box cups, pieces of plastic packaging, sequins and feathers). The teacher showed the children which adhesive (Copydex or PVA) was the more appropriate for gluing each item to the plate. A pea stick was then firmly taped to the plate. The body was made from a square of material with a hole cut in the middle through which the pea stick was inserted. The fabric was tied to the stick with string. The children then drew round their hands on thin card. These were then cut out and attached with Copydex to two diagonally opposite corners of the fabric. A pea stick was taped to one of the hands to act as a control rod. The other hand was left to dangle.

Five and six year olds

The five and six year olds made varyingly complex rod puppets although all followed the same basic design. A plastic bottle packed with newspaper formed the head. The body was made from a pea stick, with half a pea stick taped across it to form a cross. The upper part of this was forced into the bottom of the bottle head, the arms of the cross forming the shoulders. The arms, thick pieces of string, were attached to the ends of each shoulder (figure 10.2).

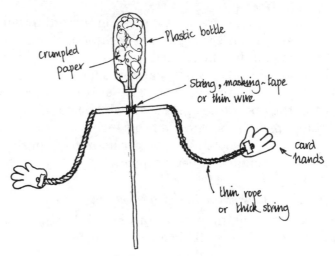

Figure 10.2   Puppet structure

Fabric was then draped over the shoulders – in some cases cereal boxes or plastic bottles bulked out the body. Features for the faces were made from crumpled paper, liberally coated in PVA or paste, and hands were constructed from shaped foam, or cut from card or fabric. In most cases, one pea-stick control rod provided animation to one arm, or both linked together.

Some of the children went on to make simple string puppets. The structure was almost identical to the rod puppets except that instead of control rods operating the limbs from below, strings were attached to the limbs and fixed to a cross-shaped frame made from stripwood. Some of the children made stiffer limbs from stripwood rather than rope, with shoulders and elbows hinged with string, wire or card, with any necessary holes drilled by the teacher (figure 10.3).

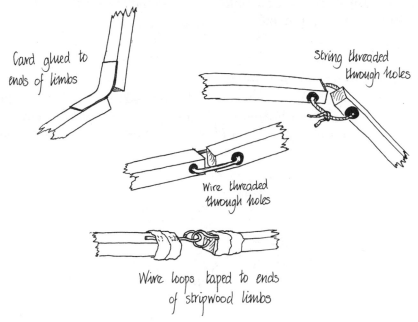

Card glued to
ends of limbs

String threaded
through holes

Wire threaded
through holes

Wire loops taped to ends
of stripwood limbs

Figure 10.3   Flexible limb joints

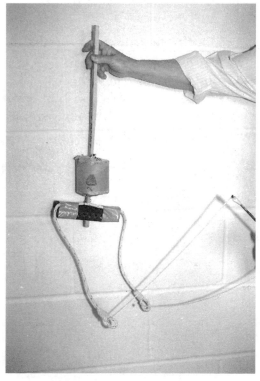

Figure 10.4   Structure of string puppet

The next round of design and make activities took place the following week and focused on hinges.

Puppet making workshop 2: hinged puppets

Four year olds: sock puppets

A sock was modified by turning the end inside-out to form a mouth into which was glued a hinged circle of card. Facial details such as felt noses, tongues and ears, and sequin eyes were glued on as necessary (figure 10.5).

Figure 10.5   Simple sock puppet

Five and six year olds: egg box puppets

A six-egg egg box was used as a basis for the head of these puppets. The children selected suitable fabric for dragons, crocodiles, frogs or imaginary beasts. This was glued to the back of both halves of the egg box and joined (with simple stitching, stapling or gluing, depending upon the ability of the child) to form a tube (figure 10.6).

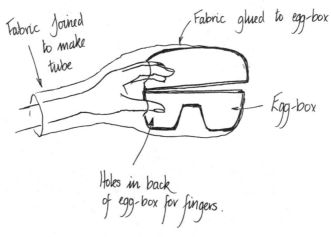

Figure 10.6   Egg box puppet

In most cases, the animation for the mouth of the puppet was provided by the children inserting fingers in holes at the back of the puppet's head.

Puppet-making workshop 3: Shadow puppets
Four, five and six year olds

The puppeteer had shown the children her shadow puppets, some of which she had made and others which she had bought in Thailand (figure 10.7). She had left some in school for the children to look at more closely.

Figure 10.7 Thai shadow puppet

The teacher used this collection as a starting point for an activity on shadow puppets. She showed all the children how movable card limbs could be made from pieces of card linked with paper fasteners (see Chapter 6) and how florist's wire could be used to support or animate the puppets. Working in groups with parent helpers and the classroom assistant, the children designed and made shadow puppets. The youngest children made very simple puppets, with only one moving part, e.g. a dog with a wagging tail, a chicken with a pecking head, an elephant with a swinging trunk. The older children attempted more complex puppets – people in profile with moving arms and legs, a dragon with a jointed tail and opening jaws, and birds with flapping wings (figure 10.8).

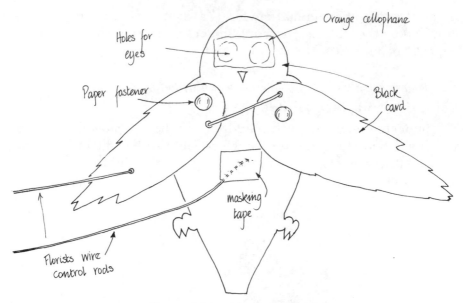

Holes for eyes

Orange cellophane

Paper fastener

Black card

masking tape

Florists wire control rods

Figure 10.8   Shadow puppet

Once all the puppets had been completed, the children worked in small groups with an adult to make up a story around their collection of characters. The stories (unscripted) were acted out to the rest of the class. A tracing-paper screen, fixed to a table with G clamps in front of an overhead projector, provided the theatre for this shadow puppet show.

Assessment opportunities

Aided by a number of well-briefed helpers, the teacher observed, interviewed and listened to children as they worked, and made some assessment of their skills, knowledge and understanding in relation to her specified learning objectives. These opportunities for assessment are indicated in the following chart together with suggestions for possible development and extension activities. Although some of the activities in this study unit provided rich learning opportunities for English, the chart simply focuses on the Design and Technology element.

Type of Activity	Experience provided	Teaching / Learning objectives	Evidence of learning. Children will be able to:	Opportunities for assessment	Possibilities for development and extension
Introduction Focused task - evaluating	puppeteer's visit: puppet show; examination and discussion of the different types of puppets	provide knowledge of range of puppet types	explain: why different materials had been used for different parts of the puppets; how puppets had been made; how puppets worked	listening to children's explanations	collections / displays of different types of materials & joining techniques
Focused design and make task	making puppets 4 yr olds - paper plate puppets; 5 &6 yr olds - rod puppets from reclaimed materials and fabric; string puppets	provide opportunity for children to convey design ideas through talking and drawing; develop children's making skills - marking out, cutting in paper, card, fabric & wood; develop children's techniques for making fixed & flexible joints; introduce simple control	explain and /or draw to communicate ideas; make, from a range of materials, a puppet which functions properly	listening to children's explanations and analysing the quality of children's drawings; observing children's making process & evaluating quality of the end product	observational drawing to develop ability to represent 3D as 2D; use of plastic & stripwood for making models in other contexts eg simple vehicles, toys
Focused design and make task	making puppets with hinges 4 yr olds - sock puppets; 5& 6 yr olds fabric puppets with egg-box hinges	develop understanding of hinged joints; develop children's making and joining skills with fabric	explain the way a hinge works; cut & join fabrics successfully	listening to children's explanations; observing children's making process & evaluating quality of the end product	studying hinges in other contexts eg doors, lids; simple paper engineering eg origami frogs & flapping birds, simple cards / books with opening flaps
Focused evaluation and design and make task	shadow puppets: examination and discussion of shadow puppets; making shadow puppets	develop understanding of flexible joints in card; develop cutting & joining skills with card	understand where flexible joining is required to create realistic movement; make successful flexible joints in card	listening to children's explanations as to their choice of joints; observing children's making processes	further activities with paper linkages (see chapter 6)

Figure 10.9   Puppet activities planning chart

Textiles

This unit was carried out by a class of eight and nine year olds.

Their relevant past Design and Technology experiences relating to textiles included collage, making finger puppets and patterning materials with fabric crayons. Although these activities had developed the children's skills in working with textiles, they had not addressed the characteristics of different fabrics and the processes involved in their production.

Design and Technology objectives for the unit

Designing skills

to develop the children's ability:

- to consider appearance and function
- to generate ideas while considering users and purposes
- to evaluate the effect of their designing

to develop the children's skills of:

- modelling and communicating design ideas

to develop the children's awareness of:

- weaving constraints on pattern design
- use of colour and pattern in fabric designs.

Making skills

to develop the children's skills of:

- carding, spinning, weaving, cutting, sewing and finishing
- working with wood

to develop the children's ability to:

- select materials for the task depending on the way that they perform
- evaluate and improve their work.

Materials and components

to develop the children's understanding of:

- how materials can be combined and strengthened
- twists in spinning fibres, ply in yarns and interlacing in weaving
- how pattern can be achieved in fabrics
- stages in the textile production process

to develop children's knowledge of:

- a range of weaving patterns
- natural materials which can be used for dyeing.

to develop the children's understanding of the properties of different materials.

Structures

to develop the children's understanding of:

- the structure of looms
- woven structures.

Mechanisms

- to develop the children's knowledge of simple textile machines.

Health and safety

- to develop the children's awareness of health and safety issues.

Technology, society and invention

to develop the children's:

- knowledge of the evolving nature of textile technology
- understanding of processes involved in textile production
- understanding of the link between technological innovation and people's lives.

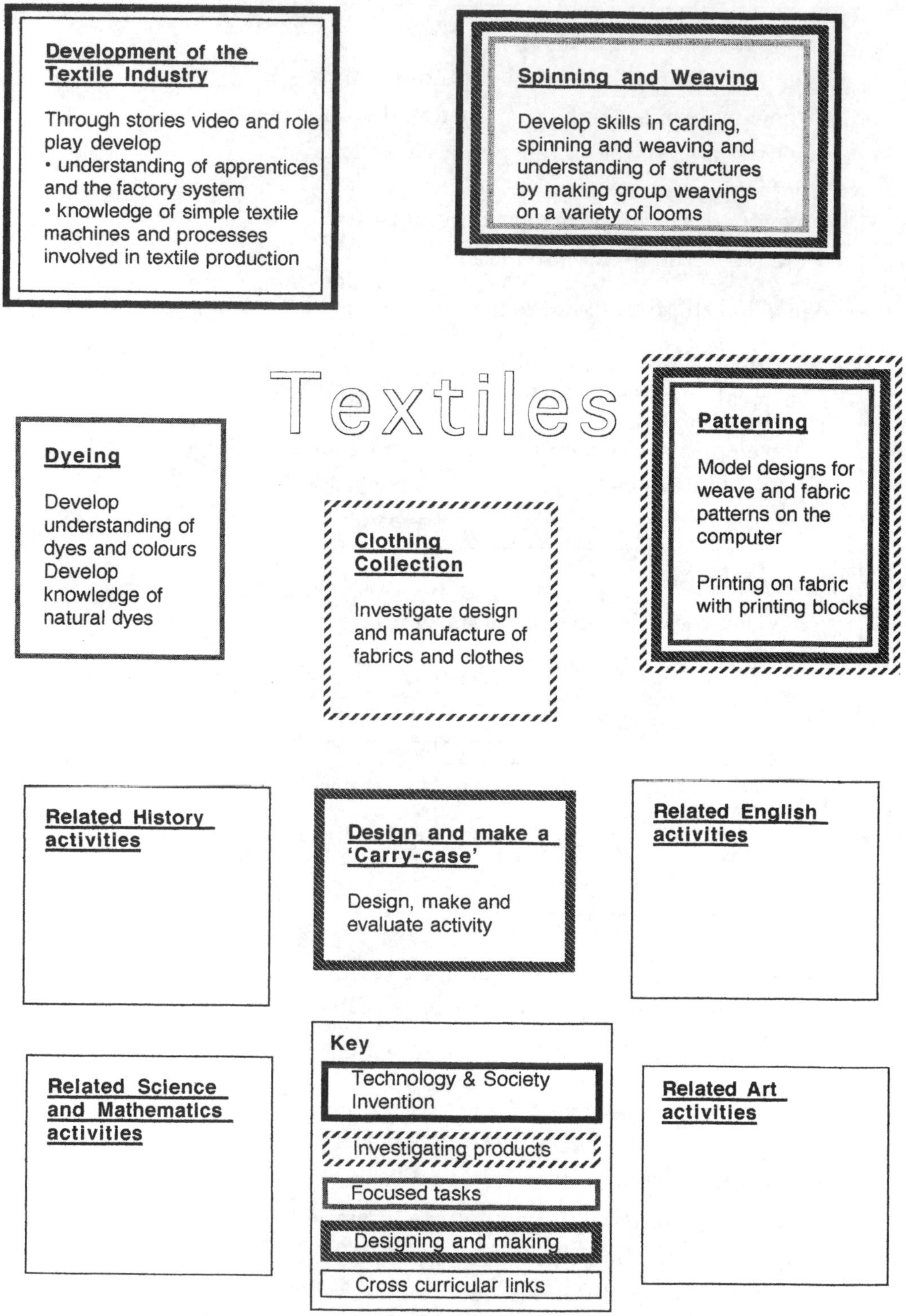

Development of the Textile Industry

Through stories video and role play develop
• understanding of apprentices and the factory system
• knowledge of simple textile machines and processes involved in textile production

Spinning and Weaving

Develop skills in carding, spinning and weaving and understanding of structures by making group weavings on a variety of looms

Textiles

Dyeing

Develop understanding of dyes and colours
Develop knowledge of natural dyes

Clothing Collection

Investigate design and manufacture of fabrics and clothes

Patterning

Model designs for weave and fabric patterns on the computer

Printing on fabric with printing blocks

Related History activities

Design and make a 'Carry-case'

Design, make and evaluate activity

Related English activities

Related Science and Mathematics activities

Key

Technology & Society Invention

Investigating products

Focused tasks

Designing and making

Cross curricular links

Related Art activities

Figure 10.10   Textiles topic planning chart

Context

This unit was initially planned to ensure that the children had some in-depth experience of working with textiles. Within this context, opportunities were identified to develop knowledge, skills and understanding not only in Design and Technology but also in mathematics and art, through pattern and symmetry. Information Technology was used to model design ideas, while historical links were forged with the study of the mechanisation of textile processes and the impact of technological innovation on people's lives. This was developed through stories and drama based on the lives of people who worked in the textile industry during the industrial revolution. Cross-cultural issues relating to textile manufacture were explored through the use of loom designs and textile patterns from other cultures.

Description of unit activity

Following the introductory activity, the spinning and weaving, patterning, dyeing and clothes collection tasks were set up over a three week block with two or three tasks running as group activities at the same time. After initial class introductions, the children rotated in groups round the activities. The children were encouraged to take some responsibility for organising their work but adult support was on hand. The design and make activity was the culmination of the unit.

Introductory activity: technology and society: stories of textile development

In this activity the children explored the effects of technological development on the lives of apprentices working in textile mills during the industrial revolution. They listened to a story describing the living and working conditions of a child of a similar age to their own who ran away from Styal Mill in Cheshire. They learned about the development of machines to spin yarn more quickly by listening to the story of the Spinning Jenny and by watching video. Through drama they explored the hazardous life of a 'Little Piecer' who worked under the large spinning mules.

Workshop 1: spinning and weaving

This collaborative activity was on-going throughout the unit. The teacher had bought two fleeces: one was shades of brown, the other creamy white. The children first carded small amounts of wool fibre using teasels and wooden carders before being shown drop spindles and the technique of spinning. They then made their own simple drop spindles by cutting and shaping dowels and drilling and gluing a wooden disc onto one end. They used their own spindles to spin a small amount of yarn.

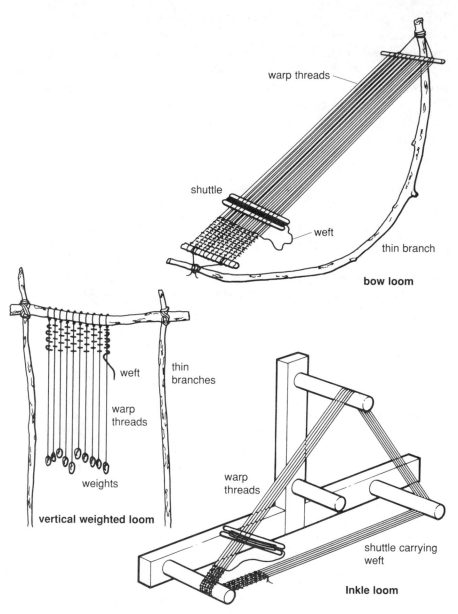

Figure 10.11   Bow, Inkle and vertical weighted looms

The teacher then introduced different types of looms e.g. bow looms, vertical weighted looms and Inkle looms, used to weave narrow bands, to show how different cultures had solved the problem of maintaining tension in weaving. Groups of children worked with the teacher or a parent helper to create simple replicas of these looms and set them up ready for use. Other children were involved in setting up a peg loom and a natural wooden frame. In all cases commercially-prepared yarn was used for the warp threads.

Each group of children who had helped to set up a particular loom took responsibility for helping others to use it. The children then added the yarn, which they had spun themselves, to one or more of the weavings on different types of looms.

Workshop 2: patterning

The children started by examining samples of some woven patterned fabrics, identifying the over-under combinations which are used in some of the better known weaves.

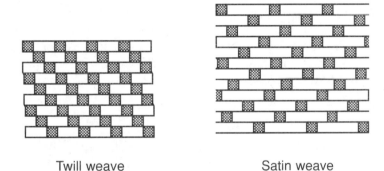

Twill weave   Satin weave

They then tried to replicate some of these patterns and develop some of their own on a weaving simulation computer programme.

Block printed patterns

Again the children started by examining fabrics, this time Indian cotton fabrics where the pattern had been achieved by block printing. They analysed how many different pattern blocks had been used and the order in which the different colours had been overprinted. The children then experimented with wooden printing blocks, bought from the local Oxfam shop, and printing blocks made from potatoes. The effects of rotational and reflective symmetry and different colourways were modelled with the aid of a computer package. The children then developed these ideas further by printing with paint on paper before transferring their ideas onto unbleached cotton with fabric printing inks.

Figure 10.12   Block-printed patterns

Workshop 3: dyeing

The teacher had anticipated that the children would not be too impressed with their weavings in natural browns and creams. She had, therefore, bought some natural textured yarns suitable for dyeing and weaving. She had also collected some books which made reference to natural dyes e.g. woad and those used in early tartans. Under supervision, different groups of children tried to colour the yarns by boiling them with different vegetable materials – onion skins, damsons, blackberries, chrysanthemum and other flower heads, carrots, tea bags and coffee grinds. A class chart was assembled with samples of the different coloured yarns and the source of the dye.

Workshop 4: The clothing collection

A class collection of clothes made from different fabrics and materials was assembled. There were swimming costumes and cycle shorts made from stretch fabrics. There were tough fabrics like denim, insulating fabrics like fleece, and wool and combination materials like Goretex, which benefit from the properties of their separate components. The collection also included items of clothing with plain functional designs and less practical garments like shiny party dresses. Different activities were organised to focus the children's attention on why the materials were chosen for each garment (see Chapter 9).

The teacher had carefully selected examples of fabric with blended fibres of different colours as well as coloured weave patterns and plain top dyed cloth. By using magnifiers to look at the fabrics the children tried to work out the way the different materials had been made. They drew the magnified fabric and recorded at which stage of the process they thought that the fibres had been dyed.

Workshop 5: design and make task: a carry case

The children were asked to design and make a case to carry an object of their choice. A design constraint was imposed – each case had to have Inkle loom bands, of the children's own design, as straps or harnesses.

The children were encouraged to identify the important elements of their design to use as criteria for the evaluation of their case: how did the design meet the needs of the user? Did the selected materials have the required properties? A variety of bags of different shapes and sizes resulted. In all cases both the strength of the Inkle straps and the comfort of the wearer became big issues as groups considered the needs of the 'cargo' and the user. Among the more unusual cases made were calculator arm bags, drink flask holders and bumbags (figure 10.14).

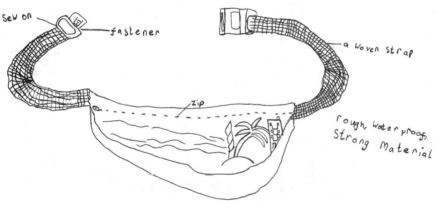

Figure 10.13   Bumbag

Assessment opportunities

The teacher made full use of a few well-briefed adults during this topic, particularly in the loom construction and dyeing activities. She also encouraged the children to help each other where appropriate. This gave her more time to observe, interview and listen to children as they worked, and make some assessment of their skills, knowledge and understanding in relation to her specified learning objectives. These opportunities for assessment are indicated in the following chart together with suggestions for possible development and extension activities. Although some of the activities within this study unit provided rich learning opportunities for mathematics, art, history and drama, the chart simply focuses on the Design and Technology element.

Figure 10.14 Textiles activities planning chart

Type of Activity	Experience provided	Teaching / Learning objectives	Evidence of learning. Children will be able to:	Opportunities for assessment	Possibilities for development and extension
Introduction Focused task	stories, video and drama related to the development of the textile industry	develop knowledge of technological innovation and awareness of safety develop understanding of simple textile processes and machines develop understanding of impact of technological innovation on people's lives	describe some dangers of mill machinery describe the textile process and some simple textile machines discuss the link between developments in manufacturing and people's lives	listening to children's explanations observation of role play	mill visit, developing risk analysis in their own work using kits to make models of simple machines
Focused task - spinning and weaving	making looms and drop spindles: carding, spinning and class weavings	develop children's ability to manipulate fibres and threads develop children's ability to drill and fasten wood develop children's understanding of loom and fabric structures	card and spin a small amount of fibre make a simple drop spindle contribute to making of a simple loom explain need for tension in spinning and weaving and make simple weaving	analysing the quality of children's spindle and spinning observing children spinning and weaving and making looms listening to children's explanations and examining weavings	using other fibres and looms making and using different types of spindle developing more complex patterns
Focused task and disassembly - patterning	investigating and designing weaving patterns (using computer) designing and printing patterns for fabrics	develop children's ability to model and communicate design ideas on the computer develop children's knowledge and understanding of woven and printed fabric patterns develop children's awareness of colour use	show alternative designs on the computer describe different weave patterns explain their own design choices	observing children designing and investigating evaluating designs listening to their explanations	investigate patterns from other cultures evaluate the way different fabric weaves perform explore alternative patterning techniques - e.g. batik, tie dyeing weft yarn before weaving, flour paste resist, screen printing using stencils

continued ...

Type of Activity	Experience provided	Teaching / Learning objectives	Evidence of learning. Children will be able to:	Opportunities for assessment	Possibilities for development and extension
Focused task - product evaluation	observing and investigating a clothing collection	develop children's understanding of the properties of materials and how they were made develop children's ability to select materials for particular tasks	explain how they think materials have been made explain why they would choose particular fabrics for specific tasks	listening to the children's explanations of manufacturing processes studying the children's design choices	testing fabrics to compare strength, rigidity, weight etc. make choices of fabric based on two or more criteria
Focused task - dyeing	dyeing yarns with natural dyes	develop the children's knowledge of dyeing with natural materials	discuss which natural dyes produce which colours successfully describe the process of dyeing	studying children's displays and listening to explanations	using some of the proven natural dyes and mordants e.g. cutch and alum, madder and tannic acid exploring resist techniques
Design and make task	making a carry case	develop children's ability to design and evaluate for appearance and function extend children's skills in cutting, weaving, sewing and finishing develop children's ability to solve a problem as part of a team	describe the development of their carry case evaluate their carry case show quality in their end product demonstrate an awareness of the contributions of their team	observation of the children at work - listening to their evaluations evaluation of the end product listening to or reading the story of development	consider modifications for reasons of economy or speed of manufacture

Bread

This was unit was carried out with ten and eleven year olds and involved 24 hours of Design and Technology teaching time. Its principal aim was to develop the children's understanding of mechanisms.

The children's relevant past Design and Technology experiences included:

Designing skills

- drawing ideas for vehicle superstructures to communicate what the end result would look like and how it would perform (see Chapter 4)
- drawing exploded diagrams of everyday objects e.g. a can opener – showing its structure and how it worked (see Chapters 7 and 9)
- drawing houses from different perspectives.

Making skills

- making stripwood chassis for model vehicles using card triangle reinforcements for corners (see Chapter 4)
- model making with Lego Technic.

Mechanisms

- linking a small electric motor to a pulley on the axle of a model vehicle – one step speed–reduction with a pulley (see Chapter 7).

Control systems

- making simple switched circuits – putting lights into model houses (see Chapter 8)
- making simple home-made switches using paper clips, paper fasteners, drawing pins, foil, etc. as part of a science activity which investigated circuits, conductors and insulators.

After consideration of the children's past experiences, the teacher identified the areas in need of revision and those for further development.

Design and Technology objectives for the unit

Designing skills

to develop the children's:

- skills in communicating design ideas through drawing so that others could implement the ideas
- abilities to explain how things work through the use of exploded diagrams and drawings from different perspectives.

Making skills

to reinforce and extend children's ability to make structures with stripwood

to develop the children's skills:

- in constructing a simple gear-box to reduce the speed of a motor, using worm gears
- in designing and making switches and switched circuits for specific purposes

to develop children's knowledge of safety aspects of working with saws, drills and hot-melt glue guns.

Mechanisms

to reinforce and develop the children's understanding of the ways pulley systems change the speed and direction of rotary motion; to develop the children's understanding of:

- the need for a mechanism to control the speed and power output of an electric motor

to introduce the children to the concept of speed reduction and change of direction of motion with worm gears.

Control systems

to develop the children's understanding of the use of switches and how they are used as sensors for automatic control.

Context

Having decided that the principal thrust of the unit should be the development of the children's understanding of, and skills in the construction of mechanisms, a suitable context was needed. Near the school was a bakery with a fully automated production line. A visit to the bakery by the teacher convinced her that this could provide a valuable context, since it would also link with some science work on food types which was also part of the term's work. After brainstorming, the teacher selected the following Design and Technology activities.

Description of unit activity

Workshop 1: baking bread

After some introductory work on food types and nutrition, the children looked at different kinds of bread from various cultures.

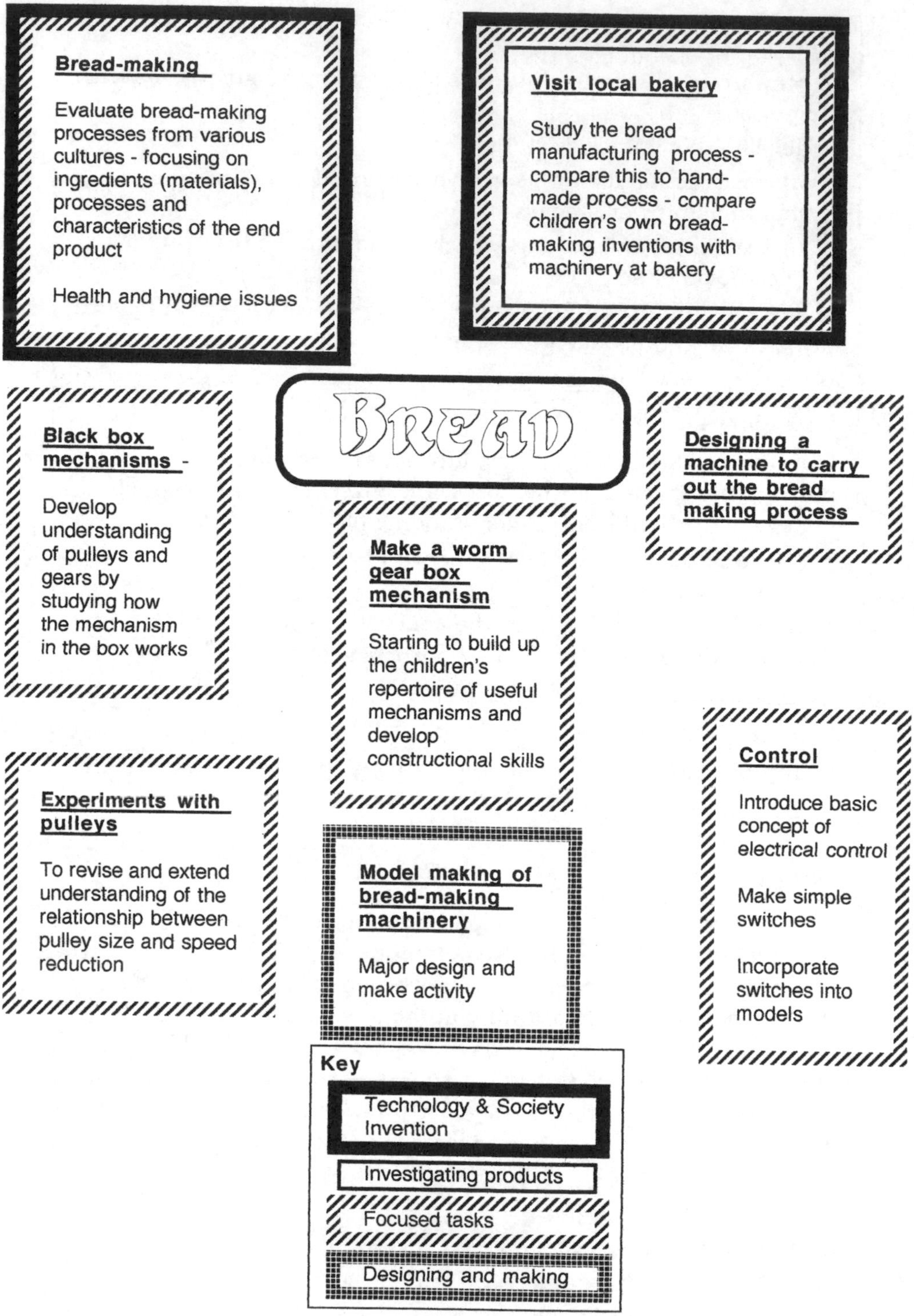

Bread-making

Evaluate bread-making processes from various cultures - focusing on ingredients (materials), processes and characteristics of the end product

Health and hygiene issues

Visit local bakery

Study the bread manufacturing process - compare this to hand-made process - compare children's own bread-making inventions with machinery at bakery

BREAD

Black box mechanisms -

Develop understanding of pulleys and gears by studying how the mechanism in the box works

Designing a machine to carry out the bread making process

Make a worm gear box mechanism

Starting to build up the children's repertoire of useful mechanisms and develop constructional skills

Control

Introduce basic concept of electrical control

Make simple switches

Incorporate switches into models

Experiments with pulleys

To revise and extend understanding of the relationship between pulley size and speed reduction

Model making of bread-making machinery

Major design and make activity

Key

Technology & Society Invention

Investigating products

Focused tasks

Designing and making

Figure 10.15 Bread topic planning chart

They compared the processes involved in making unleavened breads, such as pitta and chappati, with those which used yeast, and, working in groups with parent helpers, baked chappati, soda and leaven bread in the school's cookery area.

Workshop 2: design activity on communicating ideas

Following discussion with the whole class, the teacher asked the children to envisage, through drawing, how a machine might be able to carry out the bread-making process (figure 10.16).

To help develop the children's understanding of some basic principles of mechanisms, before their visit to the bakery the teacher set up the following two focused workshops.

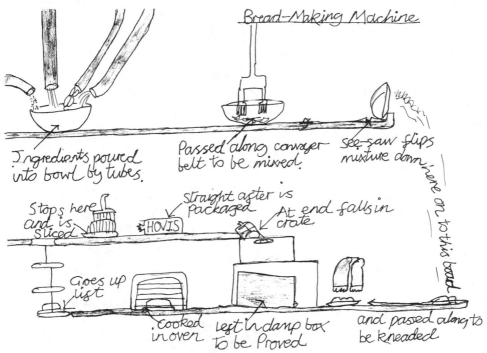

Figure 10.16 Emma's drawing of a bread making machine

Workshop 3: pulley systems

After some discussion about the way in which pulleys are used in cranes, the teacher organised a series of small focused tasks. Each activity included cards setting specific tasks and challenges. Some were based on pulley frames with wooden pulleys, others involved pulleys from construction kits. All, however, involved the children in slotting in pulleys of different sizes, and experimenting with how different sizes of pulleys gave rise to particular speed reductions. Finally, the teacher provided a redundant belt-drive record deck which showed how, in a real-life situation, the size of the shaft around which the belt ran affected the speed at which the turntable revolved.

Workshop 4: imaginary disassembly

In the second activity the children were confronted with a number of closed boxes. In each there was a mechanism but only the input and output shafts were visible (see Chapter 6). The children were asked to rotate the input shaft and observe the output; then draw in diagrammatic form the mechanism they thought was in each box. Finally, they could check what actually happened by uncovering the mechanism. The four examples used by the teacher were:

- two pulleys of different sizes providing a speed reduction of 2:1
- two pulleys linked with a twisted belt, showing a change of direction but no speed reduction
- worm drive showing a 40:1 speed reduction
- crank linked to a wheel, to show reciprocating (push-pull) output motion.

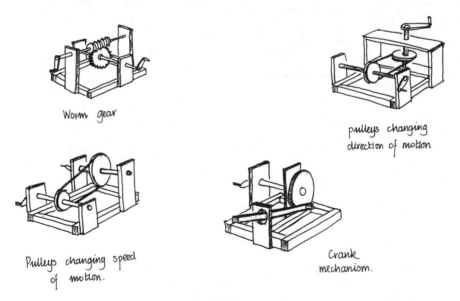

Figure 10.17   Black box mechanisims

The children were also asked to consider which mechanism might be appropriate for each stage of the bread making process – assuming the machinery would be powered by an electric motor.

Activity 5: bakery visit

The children then visited the bakery to see how sliced bread was manufactured. They saw that, after the dough was mixed in an enormous stainless steel vessel, it was tipped into a machine which ejected measured portions into tins. The tins moved slowly along a spiralling conveyor as the dough proved before being transported slowly through a long oven to emerge as baked loaves. Another conveyer transported the loaves to a device which emptied the loaves from the tins. While the baked loaves were moved along another conveyor, which allowed them to cool before being sliced and then bagged, a different conveyor took the tins back to the beginning of the process to be refilled with dough. The bagged loaves were placed (by hand) into bread trays before being stacked and loaded into vans by forklift trucks.

The children sketched some of the machines they saw and made notes about the types of motion they observed – the slow rotary motion of the mixer blades, the tipping action of the mixing vessel, the stop-start motion of the conveyor as each tin was filled with dough, the slow linear motion of the belts and the reciprocatory (push-pull) motion as the bread was pushed off the conveyor into the bags (see Chapter 7 – types of motion). Finally, the children interviewed the bakery manager to discover some facts and figures about the numbers and types of loaves produced, including the proportion of wholemeal and brown loaves sold, compared with white.

Workshop 6: making a mechanism

Since any motor-powered model the children were likely to make would require a reduction in speed, the teacher decided that it would be best to show the whole class how this could be done. On their return to school, the teacher and a parent helper worked with the children in groups showing them how to construct a gear box, based on a small electric motor and a worm gear, which would form the basis for the models which they were going to make later (see Chapter 7).

Workshop 7: design and make a model to represent an aspect of the bread-making process

With some guidance from the teacher, the children formed themselves into groups and selected an aspect of the bread-making process to replicate in model form. Four groups chose to make conveyors, a fifth group to construct the hoppers which stored the flour, modelling a conveyor with cups to lift the flour into the hoppers, and the sixth group to model the mixer-unit, complete with a mixing and a tipping mechanism. The last two groups modelled the bread slicer and bagger and a forklift truck respectively. The children now had a more specific reason to re-study the closed box mechanisms they had looked at in the workshop 4 and develop these ideas in their own models. They also appreciated the importance of the gear boxes that they had made earlier.

Once the models were completed, the teacher organised a discussion session for the whole class during which each group presented their model, described how it worked and evaluated its effectiveness against criteria selected by them.

Workshop 8: adding control to their models

Having drawn the children's attention to the automated control they had seen at the bakery and encouraged them to think how this had been achieved, the teacher then set the children the challenge of incorporating some simple automatic control into their models, e.g. to stop the conveyor belt if nothing was on the belt, to detect when the hoppers needed topping up with flour.

To start with, all the children made electrical control circuits with switches constructed from paper clips, paper fasteners and foil. Once the groups had identified a way in which their piece of machinery could be controlled automatically by using switches, the teacher gave the children guidance on a 'need to know' basis. Conveyor belt groups opted for switches operated by the loaves – as a loaf dropped on to a conveyor, it knocked a switch to turn on the conveyor. Then on reaching the other end of the conveyor, the loaf knocked another switch turning the belt off. The mixer and forklift truck groups found they needed to reverse the direction of their motors. The mixing vessel had to tip over, then reverse back up, while the forklift truck had to be able to lower and raise its forks, and move forwards and back. The teacher showed these groups how to wire a reversing switch into their circuits (see p 126).

Figure 10.18 Bread activities planning chart

Type of Activity	Experience provided	Teaching / Learning objectives	Evidence of learning. Children will be able to:	Opportunities for assessment	Possibilities for development and extension
Introduction Focused task - making and evaluating	bread-making	provide knowledge of bread-making process evaluate different types of bread develop children's skills of working with food as a material	describe process of bread making describe differences between bread types demonstrate consideration for health and hygiene	listening to children's explanations observing children at work	
Focused task - design activity	drawing imaginary bread-making machines	provide opportunity for children to demonstrate design drawing skills develop children's ability to analyse a process	draw clear design diagrams explain processes in bread making	analysing the quality of children's drawings listening to children's explanations	represent steps in a process with flowcharts
Focused task - mechanical control	guided experimentation with various pulley systems	reinforce and develop children's understanding of relationship between pulley size and speed reduction	carry out set challenges (eg. make a system in which two turns of one pulley produce one turn in an attached pulley) record findings in writing and diagrams.	observing children solving problems and challenges listening to their explanations evaluating written and diagrammatic explanations of what they found out	investigate two-stage pulley systems study Victorian machinery - eg at cotton mill or slate workshop (see chapter 7)

continued ...

Type of Activity	Experience provided	Teaching / Learning objectives	Evidence of learning. Children will be able to:	Opportunities for assessment	Possibilities for development and extension
Focused task - mechanical control & imaginary disassembly	black- box mechanisms - how do they work?	develop children's knowledge and understanding of the way geared mechanisms can change the speed, type and direction of motion. develop design drawing skills (representing ideas in diagrammatic form)	explain how mechanical link between input and output works represent mechanisms in diagrammatic form	listening to the children's explanations of their drawings studying the drawings for clarity of communication of ideas.	black boxes with more complex mechanisms eg cam and bevel gears children make black boxes for each other children make construction kit mechanism then draw it - pass design drawing to partner who tries to make mechanism from diagram (see chapter 7)
Focused task - evaluating a process	bakery visit	provide an opportunity for children to observe, analyse and evaluate a mechanical process enable children to study types of motion produced by various pieces of machinery develop the children's ability to represent diagrammatically the workings of machinery	explain the way the machines replicate the manual process of bread making represent machinery workings diagrammatically	listening to the children's explanations studying the children's drawings for clarity and listening to the children's explanations of their drawings	examine and disassemble some everyday machines eg hairdrier, coffee grinder (see chapter 7)

Type of Activity	Experience provided	Teaching / Learning objectives	Evidence of learning. Children will be able to:	Opportunities for assessment	Possibilities for development and extension
Focused task - making and mechanical control	making a worm gear-box	extend children's skills in working with stripwood extend children's knowledge of safe working practices develop understanding of worm-gearing for speed reduction develop skills and knowledge of constructing a basic mechanism	make frames from stripwood demonstrate an awareness of safety aspects explain the workings of the gear-box construct a working mechanism	evaluation of the end product observation of the children at work listening to the children's explanations of the way the gear-box works	experiment with variety of construction kits to make compound gear trains (see chapter 7)
Design and make task	making a model of part of the bakery process evaluation of the models	develop the children's ability to apply their knowledge and understanding of mechanisms in a problem solving context develop the children's making skills to meet a design brief develop the children's skills of evaluation	match type of mechanism to the task required and apply this in a practical context evaluate models against identified criteria	evaluation of the end product in relation to the design brief observation & interaction with the children during the making process listening to children's evaluations	link different models to make a system design and make activities linked to other contexts eg airport, fair
Focused task - control Design and make task	discussion of control systems at the bakery making switches and electrical circuits adding electrical control systems to their models	introduce basic concepts of control extend the children's understanding of how switches control electrical devices introduce idea of automatic electrical control develop children's skills in designing & making switches to perform specific tasks	answer questions about control at the bakery in relation to their models wire switches into the circuits in the correct places explain how their control system works make home-made switches	evaluation of the children's circuits and switches listening to the children's explanations	use microswitches rather than home-made switches introduce computer control (see chapter 8)

Assessment opportunities

As in the two previous topics, the activities provided the teacher with a number of opportunities to observe, interview and listen to children and make some assessment of their skills, knowledge and understanding in relation to her specified learning objectives. These opportunities for assessment are indicated in the following chart together with suggestions for possible development and extension activities. Although some of the activities within this study unit provided learning opportunities for other curriculum areas e.g. science and mathematics, the chart simply focuses on the Design and Technology element.

Conclusion

The above three examples show how some teachers chose to address their learning objectives for Design and Technology by bringing together a blend of focused tasks, product evaluation and disassembly, and design and make activity within a cohesive package. The contexts chosen depended on the other work that was going on in the classroom at the time. For these particular teachers, the opportunities which these contexts offered for linking Design and Technology activity with English, mathematics, science, history, and art was seen as very beneficial to the children's learning overall.

Further reading

Most books on Design and Technology in the primary school provide sections or chapters on curriculum planning or classroom organisation.

Benson, C (1992), *Design and Technology at Key Stages 1 & 2: A practical guide to planning and implementation*, Longman

Bindon, A & Cole, P (1991), *Teaching Design and Technology in the Primary Classroom*, Blackie

Richards, R (1990), *An Early Start to Technology*, Simon & Schuster

DES (1991), *The Teaching and Learning of Design and Technology*, HMSO

McCormick et al (1993), *Teaching and Learning Technology*, Addison Wesley

11 Curriculum planning in the school

Basic considerations

How is it that *curriculum planning* does not have the same ring of excitement as *designing and making*, when the processes are not dissimilar? In this chapter we examine strategies that can be employed for designing and developing a cohesive school Design and Technology curriculum, which will ensure that children have the means and the opportunity to successfully and safely develop their abilities to design, to make, to solve problems and to recognise the wider impact of technology.

As with any design brief, in designing a curriculum one has to consider the specifications it must meet. For example, the list of specifications drawn up by one group of Design and Technology co-ordinators on an in-service course included these criteria.

The plan needs
– to incorporate:

- *progression*   to ensure children progressively develop knowledge, skills and understanding
- *guidance*   on assessment and monitoring procedures
- *references*   to the national and/or local curriculum and, where appropriate, other curriculum areas
- *ideas*   which ensure continuity of experience for children and which can be realistically used in the classroom.

– to have:
- *clarity*   to be understandable and deliverable by all members of staff
- *detail*   sufficient for providing guidance, with an indication of where other sources of information may be found

– to be:

- *manageable* to ensure it is actually used
- *flexible*   to respond to the needs of individuals and groups.

There are, of course, many ways of planning and organising a curriculum and, although some criteria are common to all schools, others depend on the priorities and circumstances in individual institutions.

The diagram opposite highlights some of the basic questions to be considered when embarking on any kind of curriculum development and also the integral role of progress review in the process.

Against this backdrop specific issues need to be resolved. They include:

curriculum content

links with other curriculum areas

assessment priorities

record keeping

health and safety

organisation :   accommodation

                      resources: tools and equipment

                                      consumable materials

                                      artefacts & videos

                                      people

                                      time

With this in mind, this chapter offers a series of ideas and examples which schools may wish to consider when drawing up their own curriculum.

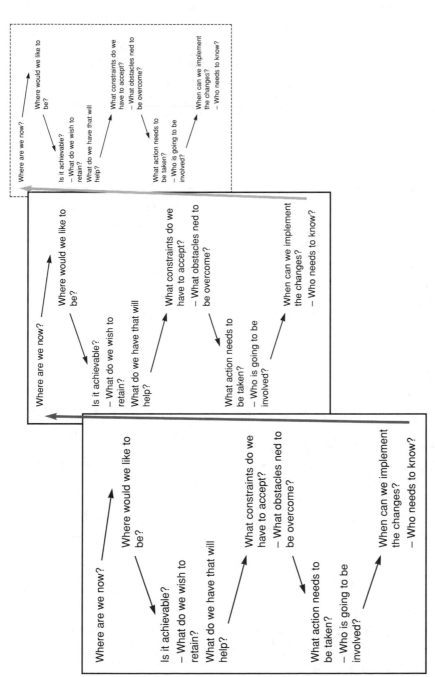

Figure 11.1 Model for curriculum development

Planning curriculum content

Rather than having to start with a blank sheet of paper, schools tend to use a variety of approaches for initially defining the content of their curriculum. Amongst the approaches often considered by schools are:

- *using the national and/or local curriculum as a starting point* and developing it in order to more closely relate to the needs and resources of a particular school. Curricula produced centrally have by their nature to be broad and general to accommodate the needs of a wide range of institutions and local situations. Considerable additional planning is required to produce a scheme of work suited to a particular school.

- *purchasing a published curriculum and using it as a basis* for the school's own scheme of work. Several publishers and some education authorities have produced their own Technology guidelines with related resource materials in the form of worksheets, cards, videos, pupil booklets and/or teacher resource files.

- *drawing upon the existing practice within a school* and formalising and extending it into a curriculum through the sharing of ideas and by relating it to published and/or legislated curricula.

Using this last example as a starting point, we now explore how this could be developed into a whole school policy. One way of making existing practice explicit and open for scrutiny is by asking teachers to put their plans down on a chart and displaying this in the staff room. A chart of this type can evolve gradually over a period of time, with teachers completing boxes as they come to plan and deliver activities in their classrooms. The chart which follows is based on the activities detailed in the previous chapter. Although incomplete, with only the plans for three classes in place, it shows how this approach clearly identifies the gaps in skills, knowledge and understanding that need to be addressed in the planning of the other classes.

There are, of course, advantages and disadvantages to this approach, some of which are considered here:

Advantages

- all staff are aware of what is happening in other classrooms
- opportunities for planning for progression are enhanced
- ideas are shared and elaborated upon collaboratively

- teachers can build upon the experiences of children by revisiting content areas, already covered earlier in the course, in different contexts
- there is room for flexibility – teachers can feed back suggested amendments
- the shared production of the chart encourages ownership of its content.

Disadvantages

- there is a danger of fragmentation – each box or set of boxes being seen in isolation
- some teachers may feel intimidated by having to 'publish' their ideas for scrutiny by colleagues
- it requires time and commitment by the staff
- ideas from outside sources (e.g. National Curriculum, in-service courses, advisers, etc.) need to be incorporated to ensure the curriculum is sufficiently rigorous in breadth and depth to meet external requirements
- it does not indicate the achievement levels of the group or individual children.

Whichever approach to planning is adopted, however, will present advantages and disadvantages but a little time spent in evaluating possible planning strategies can often save considerable time and energy later.

Once the structure and content have been defined, further detail can be considered.

Figure 11.2   Technology planning chart

	Designing skills	Making skills	Materials and components	Structures	Mechanisms	Control systems
Base Level	explaining to communicate ideas drawing to communicate ideas selecting materials in relation to design specifications	marking-out, cutting and joining paper, card, fabric and reclaimed materials making flexible joints in card	developing an understanding of the working characteristics of card, paper, reclaimed materials, fabric and adhesives	making simple wooden frameworks for puppets	developing an understanding of flexible joints	introduced to the idea of rods to control puppets

continued ...

Middle Level

Designing skills	Making skills	Materials and components	Structures	Mechanisms	Control systems
designing weave patterns on the computer considering appearance and function when designing carry case computer modelling of designs for patterning on fabric developing awareness of colour and pattern in fabric design considering users and purposes when designing products	making fixed and flexible joints with card and stripwood using string, wire and fasteners carding and spinning fibres weaving yarns making drop spindles from wood sewing, finishing and evaluating carry cases cutting and joining stripwood to make frames	developing an understanding of the working characteristics of stripwood developing understanding of twist in spinning and interlacing in weaving developing understanding of dyeing and patterning fabric selecting materials appropriate to the task extending understanding of the working characteristics and properties of stripwood	assembling and using looms evaluating and making weave patterns making rigid stripwood frames to house mechanisms	using flexible joints in card and wood to simulate movement developing a knowledge of simple textile machines developing understanding of pulleys to change speed and direction of motion	developing an understanding of the use of strings to control puppets controlling motors with switches

continued ...

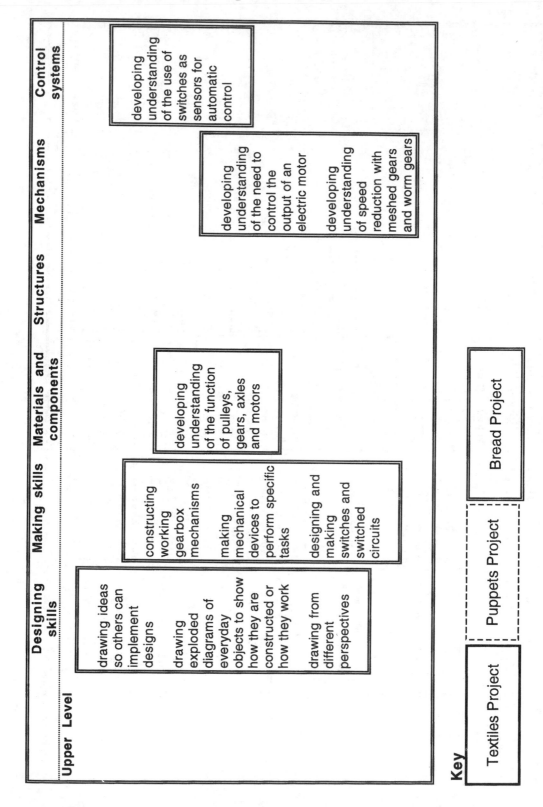

Upper Level	Designing skills	Making skills	Materials and components	Structures	Mechanisms	Control systems
	drawing ideas so others can implement designs drawing exploded diagrams of everyday objects to show how they are constructed or how they work drawing from different perspectives	constructing working gearbox mechanisms making mechanical devices to perform specific tasks designing and making switches and switched circuits	developing understanding of the function of pulleys, gears, axles and motors		developing understanding of the need to control the output of an electric motor developing understanding of speed reduction with meshed gears and worm gears	developing understanding of the use of switches as sensors for automatic control

Key

Textiles Project	Puppets Project	Bread Project

Identifying contexts and links with other curriculum areas

As has been argued elsewhere in this book, the provision of meaningful contexts for children's Design and Technology activity is of critical importance to stimulating children's active involvement in a task or project. Fortunately, because of technology's all-pervasive nature, one does not need to travel far to find suitable contexts for all kinds of technological activity.

- *Visits* to museums, shopping centres, an airport, a farm, a castle, the local recycling centre, a centre for the disabled, a theme park, docks, a canal basin, a nearby bridge, the local garage are often all that is required to invite the children to don their 'technological spectacles' to view the way in which technology affects a familiar occupation or activity (e.g. see the bakery visit in Chapter 10).
- *Studying* the school environment can make a good technological starting point: the design of the school building, the layout of the rooms, the materials from which it is constructed and the method of construction are all solutions to technological problems.
- *Consideration of the use of technology in the home* provides many opportunities for technological study. All homes abound in the outcomes of human ingenuity – from the bottle opener to the microwave oven. Even ordinary artefacts such as a collection of different coat hangers can be used to encourage children to consider the choice of materials and the suitability of particular designs to meet design criteria.
- *The use of video and/or visitors* to extend the range of experiences available to the children.

The breadth of technological application in the world around us means that virtually any curriculum area can incorporate some aspect of technological study. Science work on weather can lead to children designing and making their own weather recording instruments. History topics present opportunities to model castle defence and attack devices. The previous chapter gives examples of technology-related work which provide starting points for work in other curriculum areas.

Assessment priorities

Building opportunities for assessment into activities is, fortunately, not too difficult with Design and Technology. The quality of finish of an artefact, the level of complexity of a solution, the skills and range of techniques employed in constructing a model are all observable and, to some extent, measurable. Less obvious are the depth of thought, the designing and planning processes which a child has gone through, or the range of alternatives considered before a solution is selected. This sort of information can be gathered through discussion, questioning or (not always the most reliable means) asking the children to record pictorially, or in writing, their design processes.

When engaged in design-and-make activities children tend to apply the knowledge, skills and understanding with which they feel confident. For instance, it was not until one teacher of a class of eight year olds encouraged the children to make a model town that she found there were a number of children who did not really understand how to wire up an electrical circuit, despite the fact they had had considerable prior experience with electrical kits. Focusing on a child's approach and end product in a design-and-make activity, rather than a focused task, can give us, as teachers, a truer indication of what they understand.

Record keeping

The chart earlier in this chapter provides a clear record of the experiences of the children within each set of activities, but does not provide opportunities for recording the achievements of individual children. The ten year olds may have all carried out the pulley task, but this does not guarantee that all will have understood the underlying concepts to the same level. The dilemma which underscores the creation and use of all record keeping systems is that of balancing quantity and quality of information, with ease of use and manageability. The ideal system is one which provides the maximum amount of information, with the least amount of effort in logging or accessing that information.

The most commonly used systems employed in primary schools are:

- *tick lists* – each child has a record sheet on which progress in various aspects of Technology is logged by ticking appropriate boxes

- *portfolios* – each child has a folder in which is kept examples and photographs of work annotated with comments by the teacher and sometimes the child
- *teachers' record books* – the teacher has a separate section for each child and records details of incidents and events indicating progress.

All systems have their advantages and disadvantages, but the following questions can act as a starting point when selecting a system:

- Does it comply with national or local requirements for record keeping?
- Is there a similar system already in existence which can be modified and used?
- Does it provide teachers with the information they require for planning future work, for mapping progress against the scheme of work?
- How accessible is the information – can a teacher refer to it quickly for planning?
- How long will it take to complete, when and how often?
- How closely does it relate to the school's assessment policy?
- Will every teacher find it useful and be willing to use it?

Health and safety

The potential for accident in Design and Technology is high, but when precautions are taken many of these risks can be reduced. Good technology teaching provides opportunities for children to assess risks and control their own activities safely. Some education authorities impose restrictions of the use of particular tools or on certain types of activity with young children. When drawing up guidelines for the safe use of tools and materials in Design and Technology it is worth investigating whether there is any national or local framework already in existence which can form the basis for a school policy.

Safe working practices do not develop spontaneously. In some schools, a small team of adult helpers take time each year to work with every child on a focused task which introduces them to safe practices in the use of potentially hazardous tools and equipment. The children in these schools know they are not allowed to use these pieces of equipment until they have worked with an adult and received a safety certificate. Each school's policy on the use of tools and materials is known by all, including classroom assistants and parent helpers. Every adult takes responsibility to ensure the children adhere to this policy at all times, even when the children are not under their direct supervision.

When drawing up a Health and Safety policy, consideration of the following issues can be helpful:
• How does it incorporate national and local legislation and guidelines?
• Does it include general guidance for the use of tools and materials?
• Does it have specific information about the use of particular pieces of equipment?
• Does it take account of children with Special Educational Needs?
• Does it include aspects of health and hygiene for the handling and use of food?
• Are there existing practices which need to be examined and possibly modified?
• Is additional equipment required (e.g. safety goggles, gloves, face masks)?
• How will adults who supervise children in the school be informed about the school's safety policy?
• How will it be implemented with the children?

Organisation

The decisions which have to be made about a school's organisational strategies for teaching Technology are so interrelated that one can seldom discuss one aspect without having to consider the others. The suggestions and ideas which are presented in this section are not presented in order of priority. They aim to act as points for discussion although sometimes the school circumstances will be such that there are few alternatives available for discussion.

Accommodation

A fundamental question here is whether Technology should be taught in the classroom, in a central shared resource area, or in a room designated for Technology.

Clearly the response depends on a range of factors including the space available in the school, the layout of the school, the range of resources available, the organisation of the resources and the school's policy on teaching and learning in general.

Completing a chart such as this can help identify the strengths and weaknesses for the alternative organisational strategies open to a school.

Strategy	Advantages	Disadvantages
Dedicated Technology room	• tools and materials are in one place • work area can be designed for the use of specific tools (e.g. a hot glue gun area, a sawing area) • safe and permanent installation of equipment (e.g. vices, drill stands) • helps instil 'workshop' habits in children • more economical use of tools through less need for duplication • provides more storage space for part finished projects • easier to keep tidy •	• needs to be timetabled • could inhibit spontaneous response to children's ideas • someone must assume responsibility for the area • whole class needs to work at same time, unless plans for supervision are made – this can make it difficult for the teacher to give help at group and individual level. • ....
Individual classrooms	• enables the easy deployment of a range of teaching styles to meet the needs of the children • allows for greater flexibility when using group work • provides opportunities for integration of D&T with other curriculum areas • enables immediate response to children's ideas • makes supervision and support easier •	• tools and resources may have to be duplicated • can be distracting for other children • risks could be increased through temporary nature of tool installation • creates an additional storage problem for materials and models • ....

contiiued ...

Strategy	Advantages	Disadvantages
Central shared practical area	• many of the advantages listed above for a designated Technology room • teachers sharing the area can share supervision •	• may prove difficult for a teacher to interact with children while engaged in Technological tasks • greater risks of accident if children unsupervised • ....

Some of the problems associated with a these strategies, particularly issues to do with supervision of children, can be overcome through the use of ancillary staff. This may, however, give rise to the need to consider other factors (see 'people').

Whatever accommodation strategy is employed, its success is linked with the quality and range of resources available.

Resources

The choice of tools, equipment and materials will naturally be influenced by the types of activity which are planned in a school's scheme of work and, of course, by the available finance. The school also needs to consider how it will use other resources such as the environment, personnel and time.

Tools and equipment

To carry out Design and Technology activities, a range of tools and equipment is required to cover the different facets. The specific equipment, and its quantities, will vary depending upon the emphasis placed on the different activities in the school's scheme of work. The following headings will, however, provide some guidance as to what may be required:

Equipment for designing
• equipment for drawing – pencils, pens, ruler, drawing boards, computer software
• equipment for prototyping – construction kits

Tools and equipment for constructing
• tools for cutting – hacksaws, craft knives, scissors, shaper saw

- tools for making holes – drills, punches, circle cutters
- tools for shaping – files, rasps, sandpaper
- tools for joining – staplers, clamps, jigs, hot glue guns
- tools for finishing – paintbrushes

- construction kits for experimenting and prototyping

Tools and equipment for cooking
- cooking equipment – a cooker, a microwave oven
- equipment for mixing – bowls, mixers
- equipment for measuring – jugs, scales

Tools and equipment for textiles work
- tools for sewing – needles, pins
- tools and equipment for spinning and weaving – drop spindles, looms
- tools and equipment for dyeing & patterning material – bowls, batik pots

Tools and equipment for working with clay and mouldable materials

Electrical equipment
- electrical kits – for experimentation and prototyping
- power sources – batteries (NOT rechargeable), power supplies
- components – bulbs, LEDs, motors
- switches – toggle, reed, slide reversing
- leads and connectors

Computer control equipment and software
- suitable computer and software – to do the controlling
- control interface – to connect the computer to models and devices
- sensors and components – to interact with the computer and provide information

Equipment for health and safety
- warning signs and notices – e.g. to keep clear of the kiln when firing
- protective clothing – goggles, gloves
- for tidying away – brushes and dustpans, brooms

While there is often little choice about the necessary range of equipment required to support Technology in the primary school, the policy decisions which revolve around the ways in which that equipment is stored and organised can become quite involved and will affect the quantities of tools required. Some of the decisions will be influenced by the geography of the school buildings or the organisation of the teaching areas, but among the systems for collecting and storing tools and materials worth considering are the following:

- *designated Technology room or area* – all the tools and materials remain within this area on purpose-built storage racks
- *shared practical areas* – two or three practical areas are equipped with storage racks containing similar sets of equipment (related to the age and needs of the users)
- *Technology work stations within classrooms* – practical areas with purpose-made storage racks are set up in each classroom and designated areas are provided (e.g. for sawing, for gluing)
- *class sets of equipment* – each classroom is equipped with its own set of materials arranged, for example, on a tool board for ease of access and quick checking
- *Technology trucks or trolleys* – the tools and equipment are stored on wheeled trolleys which can be taken to whichever class requires them – different trolleys have equipment to suit a particular need (e.g. a woodworking trolley, a computer control trolley, a construction kits trolley, an 'electrics' trolley, a general Technology tools trolley)
- *tool kits* – sets of tool boxes, each containing a group-set of various tools. These are stored in the staff room or store room and teachers take the number of sets they need to their classrooms as required.

Consumable materials

As with the choice of tools and equipment, the range of materials depends largely upon the skills and knowledge which the Technology curriculum is intended to develop. Where opportunities are given to children to choose their own materials to solve their own problems, an unknown variable is introduced regarding materials – one cannot anticipate beforehand precisely which materials will be required and in what quantity. Most schools find, however, that provided they carry a stock of core materials, more specialist consumables can be ordered as required. In addition to specialist suppliers, local businesses sometimes provide surplus materials for free, or at a minimal cost.

The following headings provide some guidance on useful core materials.

Materials for designing
- materials for drawing – e.g. paper
- materials for prototyping – paper and card

Materials for constructing
- reclaimed materials – e.g. cereal boxes, egg boxes, plastic bottles
- flexible materials – fabrics, card, paper, fabrics, wire, string, fibres
- mouldable materials – clay, plasticine, plaster, papier mache, some plastics (e.g. Plastazote)
- rigid materials – stripwood, plastics
- components and materials for joining – pins, staples, rivets, paper fasteners, screws and nails, card gussets, adhesives, adhesive tapes, threads, wools, fleeces
- sundries – matchsticks, lolly sticks, rubber bands, florists wire
- materials and components for making mechanisms – syringes, tubing, pulleys, gears, motors
- consumable construction kits – for complex structures and mechanisms

Materials for finishing
- fine sand paper and polish
- paints and varnishes
- fabric dyes, batik wax

Materials for cooking and hygienic working
- food items
- washing, cleaning and disinfecting materials

Electrical components and materials
- consumable materials – e.g. wires, bulbs, batteries

Computer control consumables
- floppy discs
- simple switch sensors

Decisions on the storage of materials usually balance the need for accessibility with security and economical use. Most schools tend to combine a central store for the whole school's use with temporary storage in the classrooms for immediate use by children.

Artefacts and videos

To supplement the more standard support materials such as books, magazines, learning packs and computer software, two additional types of resources are particularly useful for Design and Technology.

Collections of artefacts can provide valuable opportunities for children to scrutinise other people's solutions to Design and Technology problems. Interesting gadgets and objects can be acquired from far off places and near at home. Coffee grinders and coffee pots from the Middle East, African shell and bone jewellery, fabric printing blocks from India, devices for the humane capture and release of spiders, tools for de-fluffing woollen jumpers or gadgets for de-stoning olives will all help to stimulate children's curiosity and understanding of design. Jumble sales, car boot sales and the junk boxes outside antique dealers' stores are rich sources for quaint, unusual and sometimes quite mysterious gadgets.

Video recordings of off-air television broadcasts are permitted for educational purposes in the UK. If a library of potentially useful tapes is accumulated, such a resource can be used to widen the children's horizons by illustrating applications of technology beyond the classroom and act as starting points for discussion or Design and Technology activity.

People

The most valuable resource in any school is people. In addition to teachers and ancillary staff, input or support for Design and Technology can be provided by:

- *parent/community specialists* – e.g. a freelance designer, professional photographer, technologist, member of the Spinners and Weavers Guild
- *specialists from other educational establishments* – local secondary school teachers, educational authority advisers, higher education tutors, independent consultants
- *parents, grandparents and other relations,* who can provide important support for practical activities. Maximum benefit is obtained when they are well briefed in the educational purpose of any task they supervise eg the development of problem solving or practical skills, or an understanding of how something works.

Time

Once a school has decided on the amount of time it can apportion to the teaching of Design and Technology, the next task is to decide whether the time is utilised in sizeable blocks, such as two or three days at a time, or in smaller inputs of an hour or two on a regular basis.

The principal advantage of a regular input of Technology either in weekly class or group sessions is that the teacher is able to respond to the needs, interests and ideas of the children relatively quickly and flexibly. This pattern of work also fits readily into normal classroom practice. The fragmentation of lengthier projects through this strategy, however, can result in momentum being lost between sessions especially when equipment needs to be cleared away. The constant breaks can also limit the depth of thought and problem solving in which the children can be engaged.

A block of time, on the other hand, allows children to become absorbed in an activity and pursue lengthier techniques. The teacher is also able to adopt a range of teaching approaches throughout these days and use equipment which takes time to set up. But, for some children, sustaining motivation will be harder over a period of days and the time gap between blocks of time can hinder progress.

There are other ways of allocating time in addition to those described above and schools usually find that a combination of approaches is needed to respond to different activities and different situations. The following criteria can be helpful in guiding decisions as to the allocation of time and the organisation of activities.

Does the suggested way of organising time:
- fit in with existing practices in other areas of the curriculum?
- allow access to the tools and materials when needed?
- allow time for the teacher to monitor the children's progress and provide support when required?
- allow sufficient time for the children to construct artefacts of good quality and develop their ideas?
- enable health and safety requirements to be met?
- rely too heavily on volunteer helpers?

Resource constraints, such as the accommodation, the availability of tools and materials and the existing organisational approaches in the classroom will also influence the way the assigned time is allocated.

Conclusion

The philosophy on which this chapter, indeed the whole book, is founded is that a study of Design and Technology does not just comprise a set of practical activities. It encompasses a much wider brief. Through constructing, children should be engaged in evaluating their own solutions to practical problems and alongside this be considering other people's solutions to problems, and how technology has affected the way in which people live and integrate with their natural environment.

A school's curriculum for Design and Technology needs to reflect all these aspects and, in its implementation, give children the opportunity to act as problem solvers and technologists.

Further reading

Whole school strategies for the development, organisation and delivery of Design and Technology often form part of various books related to Design and Technology in the Primary School. The following books provide more detailed advice or information:

Adams R & Sellwood P (1992), *The Really Practical Guide to Primary Technology,* Stanley Thornes

Banks F (ed) (1994), *Teaching Technology,* Routledge

DES (1991), *The Teaching and Learning of Design and Technology,* HMSO

Jarvis T (1993), *Teaching Design & Technology in the Primary School,* Routledge

National Association of Advisers and Inspectors in Design and Technology (1992), *Make it Safe! Safety Guidance for the teaching of Design and Technology at Key Stages 1 and 2,* NAAIDT Publications, 16 Kingsway Gardens, Chandlers Ford, Hampshire SO5 1FE

Tickle, L (1993), *School Based Research for Primary D&T Co-ordination,* University of East Anglia, Centre for Research in Visual Education

Index